終わりの時に、わたしの霊をすべての人に注ぐ。

MANGA

メタモルフォシス METAMORPHOSIS

Contents

Chapter I

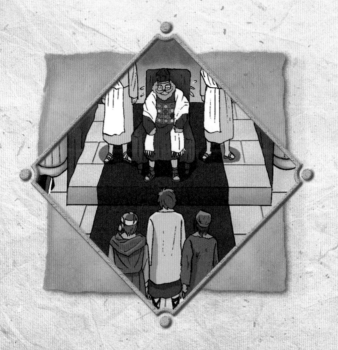

In the beginning
the Word already existed...

And the Word
was with
God...

and the Word
was God.

He existed in
the beginning
with God.

God created
everything
through him...

And nothing was
created except
through him.

The Word gave life to everything...

and His life...

brought light to everyone.

The light shines in the darkness...

and the darkness can never extinguish it.

1. Now What Do We Do?

LISTEN! EVERYBODY **LISTEN!**

YOU WON'T **BELIEVE** THIS!

HEY! TAKE IT **EASY,** KID!

WE'RE BUSY PREPARING FOR THE **FESTIVAL OF WEEKS!**

I KNOW YOU ARE... BUT **LISTEN!**

THIS IS **BIG NEWS! THEY'RE BACK!**

THEY CAME **BACK!**

HUH?! WHO DO YOU THINK HE MEANS...?

LISTEN, EVERYONE!! AFTER YESHUA WAS KILLED...

HE **RETURNED** AND SPENT **FORTY DAYS** WITH US...

AND IN THE **END,** HE TOLD US...

IN JERUSALEM, JUDEA, SAMARIA, AND TO THE ENDS OF THE EARTH...

YOU WILL BE MY WITNESSES!!

THEN... IT'S *TRUE*? HE'S...

OOHHHH!

ALIVE!

WHEREVER YOU GO...

YESHUA *ROSE* UP INTO THE CLOUDS RIGHT BEFORE OUR *EYES*...

AND WE WERE JUST *STARING* AFTER HIM WHEN...

Acts 1:1-11   9

Yeshua's death on the cross had crushed the hopes of his followers...

So news of his resurrection spread with excitement and rejoicing.

The very next day, Yeshua's followers began meeting together for prayer and support.

JUDE

SIMON

JOSEPH

JAMES

Miryam, the mother of Yeshua, and his brothers were also part of the group.

MIRYAM

There was a time when Yeshua's brothers couldn't believe he was Messiah...

But after his resurrection, they began to understand who he really was.

Yeshua's brother James became a respected leader of the church in Jerusalem...

Faith without good works is dead.

And eventually he wrote one of the powerful Ancient Texts about Messiah!

Day after day, the believers met for prayer...

Seeking God's will and longing for Yeshua's promises to be fulfilled.

Acts 1:12-26   **11**

At one meeting, Peter stood up...

BROTHERS...
JUDAS, WHO BETRAYED OUR LORD, IS **DEAD!**

IN THE **ANCIENT TEXTS** IT IS RECORDED THAT "**ANOTHER** SHALL TAKE HIS PLACE."

NOW WE MUST DECIDE **WHO** THAT WILL BE...

JUSTUS! WHAT ABOUT HIM?

YEAH! **EVERYONE** LIKES JUSTUS!

JUSTUS, MATTHIAS, YOU WERE **BOTH** WITH YESHUA FROM THE **BEGINNING!**

And the lot fell to Matthias. Now he would have authority as one of "the Twelve."

WHOA! IT'S ME?

IT'S **TRUE!** MATTHIAS IS THE RIGHT FIT!

NO-MATTHIAS!!

They decided to make their selection by casting lots...

2. Unearthly Wind & Fire

At dawn, on the first day of the Festival of Weeks, the disciples made their way to the Temple.

It was crowded with travelers from all over, visiting for the holiday.

PETER, WE CAN USE THIS ROOM HERE TO **PRAY!**

...   ...

AS YOU **KNOW,** DURING THIS FESTIVAL WE **CELEBRATE** GIVING THE FIRST OF OUR CROPS TO **GOD!**

HISTORICALLY, **THIS** HAS BEEN A TIME WHEN WE REMEMBER GOD'S **GIFT** OF THE **LAW** THROUGH HIS SERVANT **MOSES...**

WHEN *YESHUA* LEFT, HE TOLD US TO *WAIT*...

"*WAIT* TO RECEIVE WHAT MY FATHER HAS PROMISED!"

BUT... *WHEN* WILL IT *COME?*

AND *NOW* THE FESTIVAL... REMEMBERING GOD'S *GIFT*... *THIS* SOMEHOW SEEMS LIKE THE *NATURAL* TIME TO RECEIVE WHATEVER THE FATHER HAS FOR US!

SO LET'S PRAY TOGETHER... AND THIS TIME WITH *EXPECTATION!*

YES!!

The disciples began to pray fervently…

For several hours they continued…

OH! IT'S ALMOST 9 A.M...

TIME FOR THE MORNING *SACRIFICE!*

PEOPLE OF ISRAEL... AND FROM AROUND THE WORLD!

THERE IS SOMETHING YOU MUST KNOW!

MURMUR

MURMUR

WHAT?

LISTEN TO ME CLOSELY...

PETER'S VOICE RANG WITH AN AUTHORITY THAT SURPRISED BOTH THE CROWD AND HIS FRIENDS.

SOMEHOW THE ONCE-TIMID PETER OF THE PAST HAD CHANGED!

LISTEN, PEOPLE! IT'S ONLY NINE O'CLOCK IN THE MORNING! NO ONE HERE HAS HAD A DROP OF ALCOHOL!

WHAT YOU SEE HERE IS A FULFILLMENT OF THE WORDS OF THE PROPHET JOEL!

GOD SAID THROUGH THE **PROPHET**, "I WILL POUR OUT MY **SPIRIT** ON ALL PEOPLE...

YOUR SONS AND DAUGHTERS WILL **PROPHESY**, YOUR YOUNG MEN WILL SEE **VISIONS**, YOUR OLD MEN WILL DREAM **DREAMS!**

IN THOSE DAYS I WILL POUR OUT MY **SPIRIT**, EVEN ON MY **SERVANTS**, BOTH MEN AND WOMEN ALIKE, AND THEY WILL **PROPHESY!**"

BROTHERS AND **SISTERS**, THE LORD, OUR **GOD**, DISPLAYED SIGNS AND **WONDERS** THROUGH HIS PROMISED MESSIAH, **YESHUA OF NAZARETH!!**

BUT **YOU**... YOU WERE THE VERY ONES WHO **NAILED** GOD'S MESSIAH TO THE **CROSS!**

YESHUA'S DEATH ON THE CROSS WAS **PLANNED** FROM THE BEGINNING...

NOW, JUST AS THE **PROPHET** PREDICTED...

!!

!

!

THE **SPIRIT** OF GOD HAS **COME!**

!

POURED OUT...

AND GOD HAS **PROVED** HIM TO BE **MESSIAH** BY RAISING HIM FROM THE **DEAD!**

ON THOSE WHO HAVE **BELIEVED** HIM!

Acts 2:14-41

WOW!

WHAT HAPPENED TO **PETER**?!

PETER'S COURAGE ASTOUNDED JOHN AND THE OTHERS...

HE HAD BEEN FILLED WITH THE HOLY SPIRIT OF GOD. HIS WORDS AND APPEARANCE WERE POWERFUL, AS THOUGH YESHUA HIMSELF WERE SPEAKING THROUGH HIM.

AND AS A RESULT, **ANOTHER MIRACLE...**

CROWDS OF PEOPLE BELIEVED.

ABOUT THREE THOUSAND THAT VERY DAY...

ONE AFTER ANOTHER, THEY WERE BAPTIZED PUBLICLY IN THE NAME OF YESHUA.

3. More Than You Asked For

PETER, COME ON. WE **NEED** TO HURRY!

...

LOOK AT THIS VIEW!

JERUSALEM ...

I CAN'T **BELIEVE** ONLY A FEW **MONTHS** AGO...

YESHUA WAS **CRUCIFIED** HERE...

PETER!!

IT'S... ALMOST THREE O'CLOCK.

...

It was a custom in those days to offer prayers in the Temple at 9 a.m. and 3 p.m.

...

On this day, as usual, Peter and John entered the Temple through the east gate, the gate called "Beautiful."

THANK YOU, MISS...

CLINK *CLANK*

LOOK AT THAT MAN. HE'S HERE AGAIN... BEGGING.

HE'S SMART!

CATCH PEOPLE AS THEY'RE ABOUT TO OFFER THEIR PRAYERS.

A LITTLE GUILT... BETTER RETURNS.

OH YEAH... THAT GUY'S BEEN HERE FOR YEARS. PEOPLE EVEN NICKNAMED HIM AFTER THE GATE BECAUSE HE'S SO...

HEY, WHAT...?

PETER!

SHHP

CLINK
GLINK

MERCY... MERCY...

HAVE MERCY.

HEY... LOOK UP HERE!

WELL...

UM...

ACTUALLY, I HAVE NO MONEY.

WILL YOU HELP ME, SIR?

FRIENDS! HOW HAS THIS MAN BEEN *HEALED?*

I TELL YOU, BY THE POWER OF *YESHUA* ... WHO SPOKE THE WORD OF *GOD* TO YOU IN THIS VERY *TEMPLE!*

THE SAME YESHUA YOU *ACCUSED* IN FRONT OF PONTIUS PILATE!!

THE SAME *YESHUA* YOU DEMANDED BE *PUNISHED* IN EXCHANGE FOR THE *MURDERER* BARABBAS...

AND *SENTENCED* TO THE DEATH OF A *CRIMINAL*... *DEATH ON A CROSS!*

BUT HE WAS *INNOCENT* !!

AND GOD *RAISED* HIM UP... AND WE HAVE *SEEN* HIM AGAIN!

YESHUA IS *ALIVE* !!

PETER'S SHOUTS RANG THROUGH SOLOMON'S COLONNADE...

YOU ALL ARE THE DESCENDANTS OF PROPHETS!

YOU'VE **SEEN** THIS MAN BY THE **TEMPLE**... UNABLE TO WALK SINCE **BIRTH**...

BUT BY THE **POWER** OF THE NAME OF **YESHUA**... HE IS **WALKING, DANCING,** AND **GLORIFYING GOD!**

AND, GRIPPED THE HEARTS OF THOSE WHO WERE LISTENING.

THOSE PROPHETS TOLD YOU YESHUA WOULD BE COMING TO EARTH!

WHY DIDN'T YOU BELIEVE THEM?

NOW **ADMIT** THAT YOU WERE **WRONG!** ADMIT THAT YOU **MISUNDERSTOOD** THE PROPHETS AND YESHUA... AND **REPENT!**

IF YOU **RECEIVE** YESHUA AS **MESSIAH**...

THEN GOD WILL **RECEIVE YOU** AND **CLEANSE** YOU FROM **ALL** THE **EVIL** YOU'VE **DONE!**

THE PRIESTS IN CHARGE OF THE TEMPLE WERE CALLED SADDUCEES...

THEIR TEACHINGS DENOUNCED ANY BELIEF IN A RESURRECTION OF THE DEAD...

AND THEY ARRESTED JOHN AND PETER BEFORE THE EYES OF EVERYONE IN THE TEMPLE.

BUT ALREADY, MORE THAN FIVE THOUSAND HAD BELIEVED IN YESHUA...

...MESSIAH!

PETER REMEMBERED YESHUA'S WORDS...

"FROM NOW ON YOU'LL CATCH PEOPLE."

THIS EVENT WAS REMEMBERED BY THE BELIEVERS FOR YEARS TO COME. IT MARKED THE DAY THEIR NUMBERS GREW TO BE AS MANY AS TEN THOUSAND.

4. Could These Things Be True?

The next day, John and Peter were brought before the Temple leaders for judgment.

SO I HEAR YOU'VE BEEN *TEACHING* AND MAKING A *STIR* IN THE TEMPLE...

AND WITHOUT *ANY* PROPER THEOLOGICAL *TRAINING?*

BY *WHAT* AUTHORITY WOULD YOU *DARE* TEACH IN THE HOUSE OF *GOD?*

...

ANNAS (HIGH PRIEST)

HOW *EVER* DID WE GET *HERE?* ARE WE IN *TROUBLE* WITH THE SPIRITUAL *LEADERS* OF ISRAEL NOW?

BUT *THEN*... YESHUA *HIMSELF* WAS TRIED BY THESE *SAME* PEOPLE... JUST BEFORE HE *DIED*....

...

THIS WAS DONE BY THE POWER OF THE NAME OF YESHUA!

YESHUA! WHOM YOU KILLED, AND GOD RAISED FROM THE DEAD!

YESHUA OF NAZARETH IS "THE STONE YOU BUILDERS REJECTED."

HE HAS BECOME THE "CORNERSTONE."

HE IS THE ONE AND THE ONLY WAY...

THERE IS SALVATION IN NO ONE ELSE... AND IN NO OTHER NAME BUT HIS NAME... THE NAME OF YESHUA!

MURMUR

...

MURMUR

WOW! WAY TO NOT HOLD ANYTHING *BACK!*

MURMUR

MURMUR

THEY'VE OBVIOUSLY SPENT *PLENTY* OF TIME WITH *YESHUA!*

BUT THEY'VE *HEALED* THAT MAN!

WHAT CAN WE *SAY?*

ARGGH!

HE SPOKE WITH SUCH *AUTHORITY* ...

THEY *LOOK* LIKE ORDINARY MEN, BUT ...

?

GET THEM *OUT* OF HERE! *QUICKLY!*

YES!

...

5. Unity of the Believers

They began to share everything they had with one another.

The followers of Yeshua met together every day and grew in love and unity.

Often, believers would sell their land or property...

And divide up the money so that no one was in need.

WOW!

LOOK...

And gave the money to the apostles to share with the poor.

An example was set by a Levite named Barnabas, who sold a field...

The Spirit of God was powerful among them. But one day...

AND WE WANT **ALL** THE MONEY TO GO TO THE **POOR**.

PETER! GREETINGS. MY WIFE AND I SOLD OUR **PROPERTY**...

Acts 5:1-11

ANANIAS! ANANIAS?

...

HE'S NOT BREATHING!

WHAT'S GOING ON?

...

Ananias died instantly.

Everyone who heard the story was terrified...

WHAT IS THIS?

IT CAN'T BE!

LORD... MERCY!

BUT THREE HOURS LATER...

Ananias's wife, Sapphira, entered the house.

...

PETER... DID MY *HUSBAND* STOP BY YET?

HAVE YOU RECEIVED OUR *MONEY?*

6. The Apostles' Arrest

PEOPLE BECAME SO IMPRESSED BY THE BELIEVERS THAT SOLOMON'S COLONNADE WAS FULL EVERY DAY WITH CROWDS COMING TO LISTEN TO THE APOSTLES' TEACHING.

The priests and Sadducees were filled with jealousy.

AGAIN!

WE WARNED THEM!! I'VE HAD ENOUGH...

ARREST THEM!!

YOU... COME HERE!

I'VE GOT THIS ONE!

WHAT ARE YOU DOING?

NO... STOP!

WHERE ARE YOU TAKING THEM?

LET THEM GO!!

THEY WEREN'T HURTING ANYONE!

KEEP QUIET!

Once again, the apostles were locked in prison.

The next morning...

The Jewish high officials were called to the Sanhedrin.

HIGH PRIEST ANNAS, LORD CAIAPHAS, IT IS TIME...

THERE WILL BE NO ESCAPE FOR THEM TODAY!

WHEN I'M DONE WITH THEM... THEY WON'T BE ABLE TO SPEAK OF YESHUA!

THEY'RE GONE!!

SIR... THE PRISONERS... ARE GONE!

THEY'RE NOT IN THE PRISON!

WHAT HAVE YOU BEEN DOING? HOW DO YOU LOSE PRISONERS??

WHAT?!

WE CAN'T EXPLAIN IT, SIR! EVERY DOOR WAS LOCKED... THERE WERE GUARDS OUTSIDE ALL NIGHT!

ABSOLUTELY EVERYTHING IS NORMAL... EXCEPT THE PRISON IS EMPTY!

WE DON'T UNDERSTAND IT, SIR!

AGH!

WE'VE GOT ANOTHER PROBLEM!!

WHAT'S NEXT?

WE...

WE'VE HEARD A REPORT... SIR...

THE PRISONERS ARE IN THE TEMPLE... PREACHING!

MURMUR

MURMUR

MURMUR

I TELL YOU **PEOPLE**... LAST NIGHT, AFTER WE WERE LOCKED IN **PRISON**...

The captain of the guard went straight to the Temple, where he found a crowd had gathered.

AN ANGEL OF THE LORD **FREED** US...

AND **TOLD** US TO COME BACK **HERE**, TO TELL YOU ABOUT THE **NEW LIFE** YOU CAN HAVE IN YESHUA!

THE ANGEL **OPENED** THE PRISON DOORS FOR US!

WILL WE FEAR **MEN**... WHEN GOD **HIMSELF** HAS GIVEN US A MESSAGE FOR YOU?

THE GUARDS WERE AFRAID TO USE FORCE THIS TIME, BUT ASKED THE APOSTLES TO COME WITH THEM.

MURMUR... MURMUR...

YOU! DIDN'T I TELL YOU TO KEEP QUIET ABOUT YESHUA?

YOU'VE BEEN SPREADING THIS *HATEFUL* TEACHING *THROUGHOUT* JERUSALEM!

AND, YOU SCOUNDRELS, I KNOW EXACTLY WHY!

YOU'RE TRYING TO *BLAME* US FOR HIS *DEATH!*

SIR, I TOLD YOU *BEFORE*... WE MUST OBEY *GOD* RATHER THAN MEN.

WE ARE THE WITNESSES OF *YESHUA*, WHO OFFERS *HOPE* AND THE FORGIVENESS OF SINS FOR THE PEOPLE OF *ISRAEL!*

The Temple leaders hated the apostles then...

WHO CARES IF THEY ARE WITNESSES ?!

GRRR

KILL THE INSOLENT FOOLS!

And wanted them put to death.

URRR

But one man stood up, a Pharisee who was well respected by all the people.

LATER...

LET'S SEND THESE MEN *OUTSIDE* FOR A MOMENT...

I THINK WE SHOULD BE *CAREFUL* HERE...

RECALL HOW SOME TIME AGO WE HAD AN INCIDENT WITH *THEUDAS* ...

SO THAT WE CAN *WISELY* CONSIDER THIS SITUATION.

RABBI GAMALIEL

HE *CLAIMED* TO BE FROM GOD, AND *400* MEN FOLLOWED HIM...

BUT HE WAS EVENTUALLY *KILLED*, AND HIS FOLLOWERS DISAPPEARED.

AND IN GALILEE, A MAN NAMED *JUDAS* LED A REVOLT. BUT HE *TOO* WAS KILLED...

AND *HIS* FOLLOWERS WERE *SCATTERED*.

NOW *YESHUA* IS GONE. AND IF THE *STORIES* TOLD BY HIS FOLLOWERS ARE *FALSE*, THEN THEY WILL DISAPPEAR LIKE THE *REST*.

BUT IF THEY ARE *TRUE*... WHO CAN *STOP* THEM?

YOU MAY *FIND* YOURSELVES FIGHTING AGAINST *GOD HIMSELF!*

MAYBE TRUE...

HMM...

THE TEMPLE LEADERS ORDERED THE APOSTLES TO BE WHIPPED AND THEN RELEASED.

BUT THE BELIEVERS REJOICED AND PROCLAIMED THE GOOD NEWS OF YESHUA EVERY DAY IN THE TEMPLE WITHOUT FEAR.

7. Called to Serve

ARE YOU FAVORING YOUR *OWN* PEOPLE OVER *US?*

HUH? NO!

OUR FOOD IS *OBVIOUSLY* LESS THAN *THEIRS!*

CAN YOU SAY THAT IN *HEBREW* ?!

WHAT'S GOING *ON?*

UM, WELL...

I GUESS AS OUR NUMBERS HAVE BEEN *INCREASING*, WE'VE BEEN RECEIVING MORE AND MORE *COMPLAINTS*...

IT LOOKS LIKE THE *GREEK*-SPEAKING WIDOWS HAVE, AT TIMES, BEEN *OVERLOOKED* IN THE FOOD DISTRIBUTION.

HMM... THAT *IS* A PROBLEM.

LISTEN... WE APOSTLES MUST BE *COMMITTED* TO TEACHING GOD'S WORD...

PETER AND THE APOSTLES CALLED THE BELIEVERS TOGETHER.

BUT THESE ISSUES OF *FOOD* DISTRIBUTION AND GROUP *UNITY* ARE VERY IMPORTANT...

WHY DON'T WE *CHOOSE* A FEW PEOPLE WHO WOULD BE *GOOD* TO OVERSEE THESE MATTERS; INDIVIDUALS WHO ARE *FILLED* WITH THE HOLY SPIRIT AND WITH *WISDOM.*

YES!

GOOD IDEA!

EVERYONE AGREED, AND SEVEN MEN WERE CHOSEN.

PHILIP

PROCORUS

STEPHEN

NICANOR

PARMENAS

NICOLAS

TIMON

NICOLAS WAS A FOREIGNER FROM ANTIOCH WHO HAD CONVERTED TO JUDAISM AND WAS A FOLLOWER OF YESHUA.

THE APOSTLES LAID HANDS ON THE SEVEN AND BLESSED THEM...

AND THE WORD OF GOD CONTINUED TO TURN MORE AND MORE TO FAITH IN YESHUA.

MANY JEWISH PRIESTS EVEN BELIEVED IN YESHUA AS MESSIAH AND SAVIOR.

AMONG THE DISCIPLES, STEPHEN STOOD OUT AS ESPECIALLY FULL OF FAITH AND SPIRITUAL POWER.

HE EVEN PERFORMED INCREDIBLE SIGNS AND MIRACLES AMONG THE PEOPLE.

STEPHEN... I'M *SO* IMPRESSED BY HOW *DEEPLY* YOU SEEM TO UNDERSTAND GOD'S *WORD*.

I'D REALLY LIKE TO HEAR *MORE* ABOUT YESHUA, AND HIS *TEACHINGS*.

THANK YOU, *SIR*.

STEPHEN!!

WHERE ARE YOU GOING RIGHT NOW?

SOLOMON'S COLONNADE...

AS *USUAL*.

BUT SIR... MY MOM NEEDS YOUR HELP...

STEPHEN HAD FALLEN INTO A TRAP.

SOME MEN FROM THE SYNAGOGUE OF FREED SLAVES HAD ARGUED WITH STEPHEN MANY TIMES IN THE TEMPLE...

FALSE WITNESSES WERE PRODUCED WHO CLAIMED STEPHEN WAS PREACHING BLASPHEMIES AGAINST MOSES AND THE LAW.

THEY STIRRED UP THE ELDERS AND TEACHERS OF THE LAW...

AND DRAGGED STEPHEN BEFORE THE SANHEDRIN.

8. Cost of Conviction

SIR, **THIS** MAN IS A **THREAT** TO THE FAITH OF YOUR **PEOPLE**...

ALTHOUGH HE **CALLS** HIMSELF A JEW, HE **DELIBERATELY** PROFANES THE **TEMPLE** AND THE **LAW!**

WELL...

IS THIS TRUE?

HMPH! NOT AGAIN ...

...

WHAT'S THAT?

ANSWER ME!

Suddenly everyone noticed...

OH...

...

LOOK AT HIS FACE!

Stephen's face was shining like the face of an angel.

AND WAS PROMISED A LAND AND INHERITANCE FOR HIS OFFSPRING.

ABRAHAM'S GREAT-GRANDSON JOSEPH WAS BETRAYED AND SOLD INTO SLAVERY BY HIS BROTHERS.

JACOB

BUT GOD USED JOSEPH'S TRIALS, AND RAISED HIM UP TO BECOME A RULER IN EGYPT.

JOSEPH

BUT LATER, THE EGYPTIANS TURNED ON THE ISRAELITES AND OPPRESSED THEM WITH SLAVE LABOR.

MOSES

NEVERTHELESS, GOD'S PEOPLE DID NOT HONOR HIM WITH THEIR WHOLE HEARTS, BUT CREATED IDOLS, JUST AS HE HAD TOLD THEM NOT TO DO...

GOD USED HIS SERVANT, MOSES, TO FREE THEM...

THROUGH DAVID'S SON SOLOMON, GOD ESTABLISHED HIS PRESENCE IN THE TEMPLE IN JERUSALEM...

BUT STILL, THE PEOPLE OF ISRAEL WOULD NOT HONOR GOD'S LAW...

THEY SCORNED HIS PROMISES AND MURDERED HIS MESSENGERS...

SOLOMON

Please...

Receive my SPIRIT!

TREMBLE

TREMBLE

And DON'T HOLD...

THIS SIN...

AGAINST THEM.

STEPHEN SPOKE HIS FINAL WORDS...

THUD!

AND FELL ASLEEP.

Violent arrests forced thousands to leave their homes and flee for Judea and Samaria.

But the twelve apostles remained in Jerusalem.

SAMARIA district

JERUSALEM

JUDEA district

10. Ancient Text Unbound

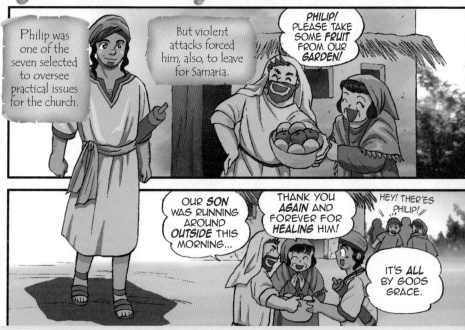

Philip was one of the seven selected to oversee practical issues for the church.

But violent attacks forced him, also, to leave for Samaria.

PHILIP! PLEASE TAKE SOME **FRUIT** FROM OUR **GARDEN!**

OUR **SON** WAS RUNNING AROUND **OUTSIDE** THIS MORNING...

THANK YOU **AGAIN** AND FOREVER FOR **HEALING** HIM!

HEY! THER'ES PHILIP!

IT'S **ALL** BY GODS GRACE.

SIMON THE
SORCERER

SO MUCH HAS *HAPPENED* SINCE I CAME TO SAMARIA...

HI, PHILIP!

I DIDN'T *EXPECT* THE PEOPLE TO OPEN THEIR *HEARTS* TO YESHUA...

AND SO MANY HAVE BECOME *DEAR* FRIENDS.

BUT THE *SAMARITANS* ARE NOT PURE *JEWS*...

I THINK I *REALLY* NEED TO GO BACK TO *JERUSALEM* AND MEET WITH THE *APOSTLES* ABOUT THIS...

BACK IN JERUSALEM...

THE APOSTLES WERE AMAZED THAT THE SAMARITANS WERE TURNING TO YESHUA.

HUH?

YOU CAN'T BE SERIOUS!

AND IT'S NO SURPRISE...

HMPH!

IN THOSE DAYS, JEWS AND SAMARITANS HATED EACH OTHER AND DISAGREED ON EVERYTHING.

FIRST OF ALL, JOHN AND I *NEED* TO GO TO *SAMARIA*.

WE NEED TO *SEE* THIS FOR *OURSELVES*.

WHAT DO YOU *THINK*, JOHN?

THEY'RE MIXED *BLOOD*! JEWS HAVE ALWAYS CONSIDERED THEM *UNCLEAN*...

I MEAN...

DOES GOD GIVE *GRACE* TO THE *UNCLEAN*?

...

I DON'T KNOW...

I *DON'T* KNOW...

BUT I DO REMEMBER *YESHUA*...

LET'S GO TO *SAMARIA*!

WHEN WE WANTED TO *AVOID* SAMARIA...

HE *WOULDN'T* LISTEN.

"YOU WILL RECEIVE *POWER*..."

"WHEN THE *HOLY SPIRIT* COMES UPON YOU..."

"AND YOU WILL BE MY *WITNESSES* IN JERUSALEM, IN JUDEA, AND IN *SAMARIA*..."

YES... THAT'S RIGHT!

EX-EXCUSE ME...

I WAS *IMPRESSED* BY YOUR *POWER* TODAY...

ZHHP!

I WANT TO *LEARN* THESE SKILLS YOU *DEMONSTRATED*... AND I'M READY TO *PAY* FOR IT.

WHA...?

...

CLINK

EVEN WITH MIRACLES AND THE APOSTLES' TEACHING, SOME STILL COULD NOT UNDERSTAND THE WONDER OF NEW LIFE IN YESHUA.

MEANWHILE, ELSEWHERE IN SAMARIA...

On the road, Philip met a man from Ethiopia who was reading a scroll written by the Jewish prophet Isaiah.

"HE DID NOT RECEIVE JUSTICE... AND HIS LIFE WAS DISCARDED FROM THE EARTH."

HMM... WHO COULD ISAIAH BE TALKING ABOUT?

"HE WAS LED LIKE A LAMB TO BE KILLED..."

HELLO... I CAN TELL YOU!

Smile

"AND JUST AS A SHEEP IS SILENT WHEN SHAVED... HE WAS SILENT."

PHILIP USED THAT VERY SECTION FROM ISAIAH TO TELL THE MAN ABOUT YESHUA.

YES... YES, I UNDERSTAND!

LOOK! THERE'S WATER RIGHT THERE... WHY SHOULDN'T I BE BAPTIZED?

AND WHEN THEY CAME UP OUT OF THE WATER...

THE HOLY SPIRIT SNATCHED PHILIP AWAY. THE ETHIOPIAN NEVER SAW HIM AGAIN, BUT WENT ON HIS WAY REJOICING.

11. Blinded by the Light

THMP

SAUL...

...

I'VE HEARD **ALL** ABOUT YOU...

HOW **YOU** HAVE STOPPED AT **NOTHING** TO FIND **EVERY** FOLLOWER OF THE WAY.

YOU ARE A **RELIABLE** MAN.

HIGH PRIEST ANNAS, SIR, I HAVE **COME** TO ASK A **FAVOR**...

IF YOU WOULD BE **WILLING** TO WRITE LETTERS TO THE SYNAGOGUES IN **DAMASCUS** ...

SAUL'S PLAN WAS TO CRUSH THE CHURCH ONCE AND FOR ALL, SO THAT THE NAME OF YESHUA WOULD BE FORGOTTEN FOREVER.

SIR, SINCE DAMASCUS IS *CLOSE* TO ISRAEL, MANY FOLLOWERS OF *THE WAY* HAVE GONE *THERE* TO HIDE...

I ASK *YOUR* PERMISSION THAT I MAY GO THERE AND *ELIMINATE* THEM.

THE HIGH PRIEST WAS PLEASED...

YOU'LL HAVE MY *LETTERS* IN THE *MORNING!*

GOOD!

AND SO SAUL SET OUT FOR DAMASCUS...

AND BEGAN A JOURNEY THAT WOULD CHANGE HIS LIFE FOREVER.

HUF

HUF

THIS HEAT...

SIR... COULDN'T WE TAKE A *LITTLE*... BREAK?

THIS IS A *FULL* SIX-DAY TRIP... I DON'T THINK IT'S *POSSIBLE* TO DO IT IN FIVE...

WHAT DO YOU THINK IS HIS *PROBLEM*?

WHY WOULD ANYONE CARE *SO* MUCH ABOUT *HERETICS?*

HERETICS STAND AGAINST GOD!

EVERY DAY WE *WASTE*...

IS *ANOTHER* DAY OF THEIR *INSOLENCE* AND BLASPHEMY!

BUT ONLY *ONE* THING BOTHERS ME...

I *CAN'T* GET THOSE WORDS OUT OF MY *MIND*...

THAT MAN *STEPHEN*...

WHEN HE WAS EXECUTED...

LORD, DON'T HOLD THIS SIN...

AGAINST THEM.

HIS LAST PRAYER...

THAT DOESN'T MAKE SENSE...

WHY...?

WHY WOULD HE PRAY FOR US?

YESHUA !!!!

!!

NOW GET UP AND GO INTO THE CITY...

AND WAIT THERE FOR MY COMMAND.

IT'S GONE...

?

ZZHHH...

SAUL?

...

MY EYES ...

I CAN'T— I CAN'T SEE!

SAUL'S ASSISTANTS FOUND HIM COMPLETELY BLINDED.

IT'S HIM!

IT'S... SAUL!!

AAHHH!

RUN!!

RUN FOR YOUR LIVES!!!

HEY...

EVERY-BODY?

OH... HOW CAN I *BLAME* THEM?

SIGH

THEY'LL *NEVER* TRUST ME NOW...

TAP!

SAUL... MY NAME IS BARNABAS.

EVEN THE BELIEVERS IN JERUSALEM WOULD NOT GO NEAR SAUL. BUT BARNABAS TOOK HIM TO PETER AND EXPLAINED EVERYTHING.

LATER, SAUL RETURNED TO, TARSUS, HIS HOMETOWN.

12. No Outsiders, No Insiders

In the town of Caesarea, by the Mediterranean Sea...

AHHH!

There lived a Roman officer named Cornelius.

WHAT A **BEAUTIFUL** DAY...

Though not Jewish, he had believed in God...

Cornelius was highly respected in the Italian Regiment.

And his whole family also had become devout followers.

ONE DAY, AT ABOUT THREE IN THE AFTER-NOON...

CORNELIUS!

SHUUUU...

SIMON... PETER.

SIMON THE TANNER'S HOUSE

WOW!

WHAT A VIEW OF THE *SEA*!

I FORGOT HOW *HUGE* THE MEDITERRANEAN IS!

IN THOSE DAYS, PETER TRAVELED FREQUENTLY TO VISIT THE SCATTERED BELIEVERS.

LORD... *THANK* YOU FOR THIS TRIP...

IN LYDDA, YOU *HEALED* MY FRIEND AENEAS AFTER EIGHT *YEARS* OF ILLNESS...

LORD, I CAN'T *BELIEVE* THE WORK YOU HAVE *DONE* DURING THIS JOURNEY...

AND *TABITHA*, FROM JOPPA...

SHE WAS EVEN *RAISED* FROM THE *DEAD!*

LORD, YOU HAVE **LED** EVERY STEP OF THE WAY.

PLEASE **CONTINUE** TO SHOW ME YOUR WAYS.

PETER PRAYED A LONG TIME.

THE LUNCH HOUR CAME...

AND HIS FRIENDS WERE PREPARING FOOD...

BUT PETER WAS STILL PRAYING.

GURGLE GURGLE...

HE BECAME HUNGRY...

AND SLEEPY.

SUDDENLY...

* The Jewish people had strict rules regarding "clean" and "unclean" foods. All the animals pictured here were "unclean."

PEOPLE FROM CAESAREA ARE HERE TO SEE YOU!

CAES-AREA?

PETER!

CAES-AREA... I DON'T KNOW ANYONE FROM **THERE**.

OH! **WAIT** A MINUTE...

I WONDER IF THEY COULD BE THE JEWISH **OFFICIALS** WHO HAVE BEEN **AFTER** ME...

SHUDDER

MAYBE— MAYBE I COULD ESCAPE OFF THE **ROOF**?

AND DON'T BE AFRAID...

I'VE BROUGHT THEM TO YOU!

PETER...

MEET WITH THEM...

LORD... YES.

THREE MEN HAVE COME TO SEE YOU.

CAESAREA

YOU **MUST** KNOW JEWS ARE NOT **PERMITTED** TO ENTER THE HOUSE OF A **GENTILE**...

YES.

SO WHEN YOU **INVITED** ME...

I WOULD **PROBABLY** NOT HAVE COME.

HOWEVER...

AS PETER SPOKE, HE BEGAN TO UNDERSTAND THE VISION HE'D SEEN.

HE EXPLAINED HIS DREAM TO CORNELIUS, AND HOW JEWISH LAW HAD FORBIDDEN HIS PEOPLE FROM BECOMING FRIENDS WITH GENTILES. THE HOUSE OF A GENTILE WAS DECLARED TO BE UNCLEAN.

BUT GOD SHOWED ME THROUGH THE VISION THAT I WAS NOT TO CONSIDER ANYONE IMPURE OR UNCLEAN.

AHH...

NOW I UNDERSTAND WHY YOU CAME SO **QUICKLY!**

WONDERFUL!

YOU WILL BE **INTERESTED** TO KNOW THAT AN ANGEL APPEARED TO **ME** AS WELL...

WHAT?

YES! THERE IS A MESSAGE OF **NEW LIFE** THROUGH **YESHUA**... THE **LORD** OF ALL THE EARTH AND THE SAVIOR OF THE **WORLD!**

While Peter was still speaking...

The Spirit came upon Cornelius and the rest of his household.

PETER WAS SURPRISED TO SEE THAT THE SPIRIT OF GOD WAS GIVEN EVEN TO THE GENTILES.

AND HE BAPTIZED THEM.

CORNELIUS'S FAMILY AND FRIENDS WERE THE FIRST GENTILES BAPTIZED IN THE NAME OF YESHUA...

AND THERE IN CAESAREA, THE FIRST GENTILE CHURCH WAS FOUNDED.

JERUSALEM

Acts 10:24-48   **103**

AND I SAW **GENTILES** WITH MY OWN EYES, **RECEIVING** THE HOLY SPIRIT WHEN THEY **BELIEVED** IN THE NAME OF **YESHUA!**

YESHUA EVEN TOLD US... "JOHN BAPTIZED WITH WATER, BUT YOU WILL BE BAPTIZED WITH THE HOLY SPIRIT."

THOSE WERE **HIS** WORDS...

I CAN'T **BELIEVE** IT...

...

WHAT WILL BE **NEXT?**

AFTER THE DEATH OF STEPHEN, MANY BELIEVERS HAD FLED JERUSALEM FOR OTHER PLACES.

Tarsus

Antioch

Cyprus

SYRIA

AND SO PETER'S STORY SPREAD AMONG THE BELIEVERS IN JERUSALEM...

THOUGH THERE WERE CRITICISMS AT FIRST, EVERYONE REJOICED IN THE END.

THESE INCLUDED PHOENICIA, CYPRUS, AND ANTIOCH...

Jerusalem

EGYPT

EVERYWHERE, THEY WENT, THE BELIEVERS TOLD THE MESSAGE OF YESHUA.

...

AT, FIRST, THEY SPOKE ONLY TO THE JEWS...

...

...

BUT WHEN THEY HEARD PETER'S STORY OF THE NEW GENTILE BELIEVERS...

THEY BEGAN SPEAKING TO GENTILES AS WELL. SOON A CHURCH WAS STARTED IN THE ROMAN CITY OF ANTIOCH.

RIGHT AWAY, THE CHURCH IN JERUSALEM WANTED TO SEND HELP TO THESE NEW BELIEVERS.

THEY **NEED** YOUR HELP...

I'LL GO.

THEY DECIDED TO SEND BARNABAS, WHO WAS ORIGINALLY FROM CYPRUS.

ANTIOCH

THE PEOPLE OF **ANTIOCH** HAVE GROWN SO MUCH IN THEIR **UNDERSTANDING** OF YESHUA'S TEACHINGS...

AND **MORE** SEEM TO BE **COMING** EVERY DAY. BUT I'M AFRAID THERE MAY BE TOO MANY FOR ME TO **HANDLE** ALONE...

BARNABAS CONSIDERED WHO, FROM JERUSALEM, MIGHT BE ABLE TO HELP HIM.

I'LL ASK **PETER.**

HONESTLY... JERUSALEM JEWS HAVE SUCH A **HARD** TIME WITH ANYONE WHO'S NOT **JEWISH**, MAYBE THEY'RE NOT **RIGHT** FOR THIS...

BUT...

BUT **WHO** THEN?

THE MAN WITH THE **SHARP** EYES!

I REMEMBER...

SAUL!

HE'S FAMILIAR WITH **BOTH** GREEK AND ROMAN CULTURE BUT KNOWS THE **JEWISH** LAW LIKE NO ONE ELSE...

HE EVEN GREW UP IN **ANOTHER** COUNTRY... **CILICIA!** IN THE CITY OF **TARSUS!**

I'LL LOOK FOR SAUL IN **TARSUS** INSTEAD OF GOING BACK TO **JERUSALEM.**

Tarsus

Antioch

Cyprus

Jerusalem

SO BARNABAS LEFT FOR TARSUS, SAUL'S HOMETOWN, AND FOUND HIM THERE.

SAUL STAYED, WITH BARNABAS, IN ANTIOCH FOR A YEAR.

SAUL'S MINISTRY WAS ALREADY, FAR MORE POWERFUL THAN BARNABAS HAD EXPECTED...

...

KNOK!

...

HEY!

CHRISTI-ANOS!!

!!

HEY!

YOU BOYS CUT THAT OUT!

THE BELIEVERS WERE CALLED "CHRISTIANOI," BY MANY IN ANTIOCH. THE NAME STUCK, AND THEY LATER BECAME KNOWN THROUGHOUT THE WORLD AS "CHRISTIANS."

OOPS! THERE THEY GO AGAIN...

THOSE RASCALS!

I JUST HEARD *JAMES* WAS TAKEN TO ANTONIA *FORTRESS...*

BY ORDER OF KING *HEROD.*

MARK... ARE YOU *SURE?*

WHAT DID THEY *CHARGE* HIM WITH?

THEY CHARGED HIM WITH *TREASON*- AGAINST ROME.

P- PETER!

MARK, LET'S GET EVERYONE TOGETHER...

YES!

WE NEED TO START *PRAYING.*

LET'S *GO!*

BUT PETER- WHAT DO YOU *THINK...*

IT'S *NOT* LOOKING GOOD!

KING *HEROD'S* TRYING TO *EXECUTE* HIM WITHOUT A *TRIAL!*

WHAT?

WE JUST HAVE TO PRAY!

EVERYONE!

EVERYONE PRAY FOR JAMES'S RELEASE!

THAT DAY, ALL THE CHRISTIANS IN JERUSALEM...

PRAYED FERVENTLY FOR JAMES.

BUT...

PETER... JOHN...

IT'S...

IT'S JAMES...

I *WONDER* IF THE PEOPLE MIGHT ENJOY A *PUBLIC* EXECUTION...

AFTER *PASSOVER* PERHAPS.

FOR EIGHT DAYS PETER WAS KEPT IN PRISON WITH FOUR SQUADS OF SOLDIERS GUARDING HIM DAY AND NIGHT.

OF COURSE...

THE BELIEVERS WERE PRAYING CONSTANTLY.

BUT AFTER SEEING WHAT HAD HAPPENED TO JAMES, IT WASN'T EASY TO REMAIN HOPEFUL.

...

ANDREW...

OH, PETER...

ANTONIA FORTRESS

UNGH...

I CAN'T BELIEVE I'VE BEEN *HANGING* LIKE THIS FOR *EIGHT* DAYS...

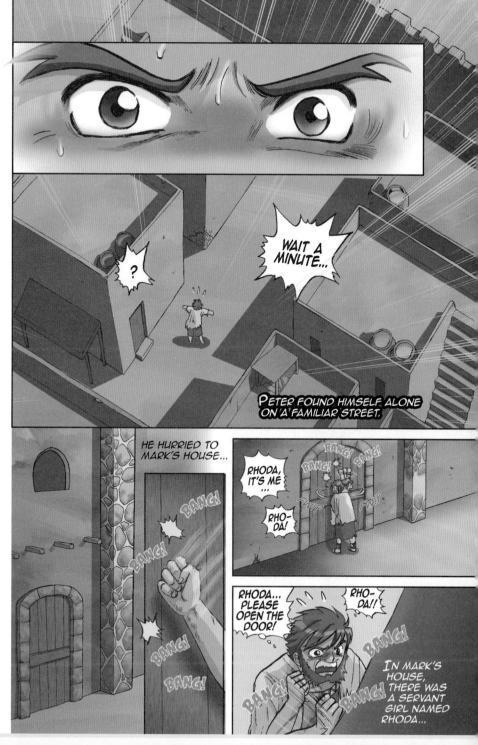

SHE HAD BEEN PRAYING WITH THE OTHERS FOR PETER'S RELEASE.
WHEN SHE HEARD PETER'S VOICE, SHE WAS SO SURPRISED THAT SHE FORGOT TO OPEN THE DOOR.
??
J- JOHN!
?
JOHN... JOHN...!
THE DOOR ...
P-
PE...?
PE- PE-
P- P- PETER!
PETER'S AT THE DOOR!
RHODA... HAVE YOU LOST YOUR MIND?
WHO DO YOU THINK WE'RE PRAYING FOR?
BUT... NO...
IT'S PETER'S VOICE!
I'M AFRAID...
PETER IS DEAD.
AN-DREW...
WOBBLE

TOO *LOUD* AS ALWAYS!

RHODA, GET THE DOOR QUICKLY!

MNG ...

LISTEN... NO ONE EVEN *KNOWS* I'M *GONE...*

IT'S *REALLY* HIM!

YOU WON'T *BELIEVE* WHAT HAPPENED!

PETER DESCRIBED HOW AN ANGEL HAD RESCUED HIM AND GUIDED HIM PAST SIXTEEN SOLDIERS.

HE DECIDED HE WOULD HIDE FOR A WHILE... AND, AFTER TURNING HIS RESPONSIBILITIES OVER TO JAMES, YESHUA'S BROTHER, HE DISAPPEARED INTO THE NIGHT.

PETER DIDN'T APPEAR PUBLICLY AGAIN UNTIL THE DEATH OF HEROD AGRIPPA.

WHEN HEROD LEARNED OF PETER'S ESCAPE, HE ORDERED THAT ALL SIXTEEN OF PETER'S GUARDS BE EXECUTED.

KILL THEM!

Wait... but sir...

HAVE MERCY ON US!

WAIT!

NO!!!

I'M NOT READY TO DIE!

YOUR HIGHNESS!!!

KING HEROD WAS MERCILESS TOWARD HIS SERVANTS.

WORTHLESS FOOLS!

It wasn't long before Herod's pride got the better of him.

YAAY!

HURRAY!

YAAY!

During a ceremony of peace between Herod and the nations of Tyre and Sidon, the huge crowd became enthralled by King Herod's speech.

HAIL KING HEROD!!

THE EVER-WISE KING!

THERE IS NO ONE LIKE THIS MAN!

PRAISE TO KING HEROD!

Acts 12:19-23   **125**

THE KING'S VOICE IS THE VOICE OF A GOD...

NOT OF A MAN!

WHAT'S THAT?

ARE THEY CALLING ME A GOD?

WELL... I AM LIKE GOD TO THEM.

AFTER ALL, THEIR VERY *LIVES* ARE IN MY *HANDS!*

BWA HA HA HA HA

HEROD FOOLISHLY REVELED IN THE PRAISES OF THE PEOPLE...

HE DIDN'T GIVE GLORY TO GOD...

AND AN ANGEL OF THE LORD STRUCK HIM DOWN ON THE SPOT.

OH... ACH! MY— MY *GUT...*

SIR....?

FOR FIVE DAYS HEROD SUFFERED... AND THEN HE DIED AT THE AGE OF FIFTY-FOUR.

WOW!!

ANTIOCH IS **HUGE!** THIRD BIGGEST CITY AFTER ROME AND **ALEXANDRIA...**

YOU CAN **FEEL** THE ENERGY...

AND SO MANY... **PRETTY GIRLS!**

UNCLE BARNABAS... THIS IS **AWESOME!**

OH BOY

OH BOY

BARNABAS HAD A NEPHEW NAMED MARK.

YOUR NEPHEW IS REALLY **LOUD**, BARNABAS.

HA! HE'S JUST **YOUNG...**

HO HO HO

HE'S BEEN CHATTERING THE ENTIRE TRIP...

THIS IS **GOOD** FOR HIM...

HE'LL BE A **FAITHFUL** DISCIPLE OF **YESHUA** ONE DAY.

When a famine struck Jerusalem...

Barnabas and Saul brought money to the believers.

Acts 12:25–13:3   **127**

BESIDES BARNABAS AND SAUL, THERE WERE THREE OTHER CORE LEADERS IN THE CHURCH OF ANTIOCH.

LUCIUS OF CYRENE

MANAEN (CHILDHOOD COMPANION OF HEROD ANTIPAS)

And on the return trip, Barnabas invited his nephew Mark to accompany them.

SIMEON OF ETHIOPIA

ONE DAY, WHILE THESE FIVE WERE FASTING AND PRAYING TOGETHER...

FLUTTER
FLUTTER

SHFAAAAA

I WANT YOU TO SET APART...

BARNABAS AND SAUL.

THERE IS SPECIAL WORK I WANT THEM TO DO.

DO YOU HEAR THAT?

IT'S THE HOLY SPIRIT...

IT'S A MESSAGE FROM GOD!

And so Barnabas and Saul were commissioned to leave Antioch and to carry the good news of Yeshua to the world.

This was Barnabas and Saul's first official missionary journey.

Chapter II

16. Unstoppable Good News

SAUL (WHO HAD BECOME KNOWN AS PAUL), BARNABAS, AND THEIR NEW ASSISTANT, MARK, SET OUT FOR BARNABAS'S HOMETOWN ON THE ISLAND OF CYPRUS.

LOOK AT THE SEA! IT'S UNBELIEVABLE!

APOSTLE PAUL! APOSTLE PAUL!

MARK, I'LL SAY IT *AGAIN*... JUST CALL ME *PAUL*.

WHAT ENERGY!

THEY STOPPED FIRST AT SALAMIS.

WHEREVER THEY WENT, PAUL AND BARNABAS ENTERED THE LOCAL SYNAGOGUE AND PREACHED ABOUT YESHUA.

FROM TOWN TO TOWN THEY CONTINUED UNTIL THEY REACHED THE CITY OF PAPHOS.

SWSSH...

SWSSH...

AHH... ANOTHER *BEAUTIFUL* DAY.

YOU KNOW **APHRODITE**, THE GREEK **GODDESS** OF BEAUTY AND LOVE...

EVERYONE **UNDERSTANDS** SHE WAS BORN IN A TOWN ON THIS **ISLAND** BECAUSE OF THE GREAT **BEAUTY** HERE.

GOVERNOR OF CYPRUS
SERGIUS PAULUS

IT'S NOT HARD TO **BELIEVE**...

IS IT, MY FRIENDS?

WELL... THIS IS A **BEAUTIFUL** PLACE.

SWEET BREEZE...

THE GOVERNOR WAS A MAN OF EXTENSIVE KNOWLEDGE AND LEARNING...

HE ASKED BARNABAS AND PAUL TO VISIT HIM BECAUSE HE WANTED TO LEARN THE TEACHING OF YESHUA.

BUT ONE OF THE GOVERNOR'S ATTENDANTS WAS NOT HAPPY...

...

Argh!

ELYMAS
(JEWISH FALSE PROPHET AND SORCERER)

Acts 13:4-13   **133**

The crowd trembled before the power in Paul's voice...

MURMUR

And darkness came over Elymas's eyes so that he needed someone to lead him.

HELP... SOMEONE HELP ME!

WOBBLE

WOBBLE

MURMUR

THE GOVERNOR STOOD AMAZED BEFORE PAUL AND BARNABAS AND BELIEVED IN YESHUA.

THIS MUST BE THE WORK OF THE TRUE GOD!

AND SO THE MINISTRY IN CYPRUS WAS BLESSED BY GOD.

I WANT TO LEARN MORE ABOUT WHAT YOU'RE SAYING...

ME TOO!

BUT MARK...

...

MARK WAS NO LONGER ABLE TO ENJOY THE EXCITEMENT OF THE JOURNEY.

Antioch

Seleucia

Perga

Cyprus

Salamis

Paphos

IN PAPHOS, THE THREE COMPANIONS BOARDED A SHIP HEADED FOR PERGA.

WHAT'S UP WITH **MARK?**

...

HE'S SO *QUIET...*

IN PERGA...

UNCLE, I **CAN'T** GO ON WITH YOU ANY **FARTHER...**

HUH?

WHAT IS HE SAYING?

MARK HAD BEGUN TO FEEL RESENTMENT TOWARD PAUL, WHO WAS NATURALLY MORE ASSERTIVE THAN MARK'S UNCLE BARNABAS.

M-MARK!

OUR **GROUP** HAS... CHANGED.

I'M *SORRY.*

MARK HAD RECEIVED EVERYTHING HE COULD WANT AS A CHILD, AND PERHAPS THE LONG AND DIFFICULT JOURNEY WAS TOO MUCH FOR HIM.

PAUL AND BARNABAS CONTINUED TO ANTIOCH OF PISIDIA...

WHEN THEY ARRIVED, THE PEOPLE WELCOMED THEM AND LISTENED EAGERLY TO THE TEACHINGS OF YESHUA.

BUT WHEN THE JEWISH LEADERS SAW THE CROWDS GATHERING, THEY BECAME JEALOUS.

Iconium

Antioch of *Pisidia*

CILICIA

Perga

PLEASE COME AGAIN *SOON.*

WHEN THE JEWISH LEADERS OPPOSED THEM, PAUL AND BARNABAS SPOKE OUT WITH POWER...

BUT YOU *RESIST* THE SPIRIT AND JUDGE YOURSELVES *UNWORTHY* OF THE ETERNAL *LIFE* GOD OFFERS!

GOD HAS *OFFERED* HIS WORD TO *YOU* FIRST, SINCE YOU ARE THE *JEWS*...

AND LOOK...

YEAH!

HOORAY

HMPH!

CLAP

CLAP

CLAP

THE GOOD *NEWS* WILL GO TO THE *GENTILES!*

THE JEWISH LEADERS BECAME SO ANGRY THAT THEY LIED AGAINST PAUL AND BARNABAS AND INCITED THE TOWN OFFICIALS TO DRIVE THEM AWAY.

SO PAUL AND BARNABAS SHOOK THE DUST OFF THEIR FEET AND LEFT FOR ICONIUM.

When they reached Iconium...

The response was similar to that in Antioch of Pisidia.

The people believed, and the leaders became angry.

THEY WERE SO ANGRY THAT THEY SOUGHT OUT PAUL AND BARNABAS TO STONE THEM...

BUT THE TWO MEN HEARD THEY WERE COMING AND ESCAPED TO LYSTRA.

Acts 13:14–14:6 **139**

17. Are These the Gods?

WHAT A **CROWD** ...

LET'S GO **HEAR** THIS NEW TEACHING **!!**

WHO ARE **THESE** GUYS?

PEOPLE OF LYSTRA,

I **KNOW** YOU ARE A DEVOTED PEOPLE...

AND A PEOPLE WHO **FEAR** GOD. I HAVE SEEN YOUR **ALTARS** ...

AND STATUES WITH MANY PEOPLE PRAYING TO THEM.

WE HAVE A **MESSAGE** FOR YOU FROM THE GOD WHO CREATED THE **UNIVERSE**...

...

THERE WAS A MAN SITTING ON THE FLOOR, LISTENING CLOSELY TO PAUL'S MESSAGE.

...

HE WASN'T ABLE TO STAND WITH THE REST OF THE CROWD, OR TO WALK AT ALL...

TH- THE ONE **TRUE** GOD...?

HE HAD BEEN DISABLED SINCE BIRTH.

THE CITY ROARED WITH EXCITEMENT AS NEWS OF THE MIRACLE SPREAD...

YAAAY!

YAAAY!

YAAAY!

TAKE THEM TO THE GATES...!

!!!

YAAAY!

TO THE CITY GATES...!

THE SHOUTING CROWDS LIFTED PAUL AND BARNABAS AND CARRIED THEM THROUGH THE STREETS.

MIGHTY GOD ZEUS...

WELCOME !!!

GREAT LORD HERMES!!

I'M ZEUS ...?

...

AGHH! THE PRIEST OF ZEUS...!

148   Acts 14:7-20

BEFORE WE REST, LET US **REPORT** ALL THAT HAS **HAPPENED!**

CAN YOU **GATHER** EVERY-ONE?

YES!

18. The First Wave

Iconium

Antioch of Pisidia

Lystra • Derbe

Antioch

Seleucia

CILICIA

Perga

Attalia

Salamis
Cyprus

Paphos

That evening, Paul and Barnabas told the stories of their adventures and the wonderful work God had been doing everywhere they went.

But the two men knew their traveling days were not over. They would need to return to those places to encourage the new believers and the churches.

Interestingly enough, in years to come, they made efforts to revisit places like Lystra and Iconium, where they had at one time been attacked and nearly killed.

WHAT A **BREEZE**, EH, BARNABAS? SEEMS LIKE A NICE SEASON AHEAD.

WHAT DO YOU THINK, BARNABAS...?

IS IT TIME TO VISIT OUR **BROTHERS** AGAIN?

MAKES ME WANT TO **TRAVEL** AGAIN...

PAUL, I WAS **ALSO** THINKING IT MIGHT BE TIME FOR ANOTHER **MISSIONARY** JOURNEY...

!

GREAT!

LET'S MAKE PLANS...

BARNABAS AND PAUL IMMEDIATELY BEGAN CONSIDERING THEIR NEXT JOURNEY...

WHAT ?!

BUT AS THEY MADE THEIR PLANS...

ARE YOU **SERIOUSLY** THINKING ABOUT TAKING **HIM** AGAIN?

YES.

WE SHOULD GIVE **MARK** A SECOND CHANCE.

Acts 15:36-41   **153**

WHEREVER IT **LEADS,** WE'RE IN THE HANDS OF THE **LORD...**

...

AND THE **ROAD...?**

...

WE DON'T **KNOW** WHERE IT WILL TAKE US... BUT **HE** DOES. AND IT'S FOR HIS PURPOSES.

LORD ...

LATER, MARK SERVED AS TRANSLATOR FOR PETER AND THEN AS SECRETARY TO PAUL IN ROME...

EVENTUALLY, HE WROTE THE BOOK FOR WHICH HE IS MOST WELL-KNOWN, THE GOSPEL OF MARK.

MY LORD!! ...

21. The Apprentice

LYSTRA IN LYCAONIA

PEOPLE OF LYSTRA!

IT IS TIME...

TIME FOR YOU TO **MEET** THE ONE WHO DIED FOR **YOU...**

MURMUR

MURMUR

156 Acts 15:36-41; 16:1-5

TIMOTHY ... TAKE A LOOK AT **THESE** TWO...

MURMUR

??

HA HA

WHERE COULD THEY BE **FROM?**

TIM...?

MURMUR

IT'S THE RABBI...

IT – IT'S **HIM...**

!

WAIT!

RABBI... RABBI... **PLEASE** TEACH ME THE WAY OF GOD!

WHAT'S THAT...?

YOU SPEAK **HEBREW?**

I LOOK LIKE MY **FATHER,** WHO IS **GREEK** ...

BUT MY MOTHER IS A **JEW!**

...

...

SO, TIMOTHY BECAME A THIRD MEMBER OF THE PARTY...

AND HE WAS CIRCUMCISED SO THAT THE LOCAL JEWS WOULD NOT BE OFFENDED.

WHERE ARE WE?

PAUL— WE'RE IN TROAS.

RABBI !

YOUR BODY IS SEVERELY FATIGUED.

IT'S A LONG WAY...

ALL THE WAY FROM ANTIOCH...

WHO ARE YOU?

FORGIVE ME. MY NAME IS LUKE. I'M A DOCTOR.

I'D LIKE TO SUGGEST THAT GOD LED YOU TO ME, BECAUSE I, TOO, AM A CHRISTIAN... AND ORIGINALLY FROM ANTIOCH.

I'VE WANTED TO MEET YOU...

I'VE HEARD SO MUCH ABOUT YOUR WORK...

REALLY?

WOW! GOD DOES DO AMAZING THINGS...

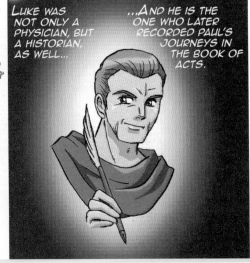

LUKE WAS NOT ONLY A PHYSICIAN, BUT A HISTORIAN, AS WELL...

...AND HE IS THE ONE WHO LATER RECORDED PAUL'S JOURNEYS IN THE BOOK OF ACTS.

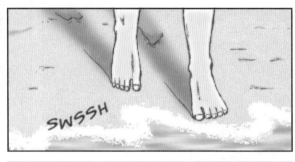

...

MACEDONIA!!

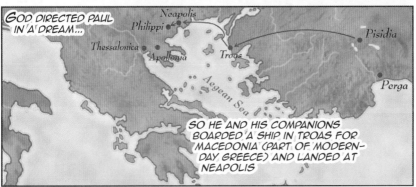

GOD DIRECTED PAUL IN A DREAM...

Neapolis
Philippi
Thessalonica
Apollonia
Troas
Pisidia
Perga
Aegean Sea

SO HE AND HIS COMPANIONS BOARDED A SHIP IN TROAS FOR MACEDONIA (PART OF MODERN-DAY GREECE) AND LANDED AT NEAPOLIS

PHILIPPI
(A CITY IN MACEDONIA)

RABBI... AREN'T THESE WOMEN PRAYING?

THEY'RE JEWISH, I THINK...

LET'S CHECK IT OUT!

?

HUH? UM... SHALOM!

SHALOM, SISTERS!

SOON PAUL WAS SHARING ABOUT THE LIFE OF YESHUA WITH THE WOMEN...

...WHO LISTENED CLOSELY TO EVERYTHING HE SAID.

ONE, WEALTHY GENTILE WOMAN WAS ESPECIALLY MOVED...

I'VE NEVER **HEARD** OF THIS KIND OF LOVE BEFORE...

LYDIA

PAUL... WILL YOU BAPTIZE **ME** TODAY?

YES!!

MY LADY...

LYDIA AND HER FAMILY BECAME SOME OF THE FIRST IN EUROPE TO BELIEVE IN YESHUA...

PAUL AND HIS COMPANIONS STAYED WITH THEM IN PHILIPPI ALMOST THREE MONTHS.

23. Power Encounter

ESPECIALLY THE SLAVE GIRL'S OWNERS, WHO HAD USED HER TO EARN MONEY WITH HER FORTUNE-TELLING...

AARRGH! HER FORTUNE-TELLING POWERS ARE *GONE!!*

I - I'M SORRY, I JUST DON'T *KNOW...*

HER OWNERS DRAGGED PAUL AND SILAS INTO COURT.

THESE JEWS... !!

!!

THEY WERE BEATEN WITHOUT MERCY.

SSRAKK!!

SSRAKK!!

UGH!

AHH!

SSRAKK!!

HUF

HUF

HUF

SILAS... ARE YOU OK?

YES...

WOW! I DIDN'T KNOW IF I'D *SURVIVE* THAT...

AND ALL *THIS*...

JUST BECAUSE WE LOOK *JEWISH*?

I GUESS PEOPLE DON'T LIKE JEWS MUCH AROUND HERE...

CLINK CLANK

AND LUKE, *TOO*, I HOPE. ANYWAY...

LET'S THANK GOD...

YES.

I THINK *TIMOTHY* WAS ABLE TO ESCAPE BECAUSE HE LOOKS *GREEK*...

YEAH! THAT'S GOOD.

AAAHHH

GIVE THANKS TO THE LORD, FOR HE IS GOOD!

HIS LOVE ENDURES FOREVER!

HEY! DO YOU *HEAR* THAT?

IT *SOUNDS* LIKE...

HUH?

SINGING !!

Acts 16:16-40

Acts 16:16-40

The judges were terrified when they learned Paul and Silas were Roman citizens...

OH NO!

I DIDN'T KNOW...!

At that time, serious punishments were dealt out to those who mistreated a Roman citizen.

THE JUDGES APOLOGIZED REPEATEDLY... AND ASKED PAUL AND SILAS TO LEAVE PHILIPPI.

BUT A NEW CHURCH HAD BEEN FORMED... SO PAUL ASKED LUKE TO STAY AND HELP IT GET STARTED.

Letter to the Believers in Philippi

The church in Philippi was known to be devout and faithful.

Paul wrote the believers in Philippi a letter of encouragement ...

KEEP YOUR EYES ON THE *GOAL!*

AND *RUN* FOR IT!

FORGET WHAT'S BEHIND YOU, AND FACE THE *FUTURE!*

OLD LIFE

GOAL

YESHUA

Flop

BUT FOR YOU WHO CARE ONLY ABOUT THE PLEASURES OF THIS LIFE...

FOR-GET GOD!

WATCH OUT! DESTRUCTION IS NEAR!

BUT *OUR* HOME IS IN *HEAVEN!*

WE'RE ONLY *TRAVELERS* HERE, LOOKING *AHEAD* TO OUR HOME!

Even from prison, Paul encouraged the believers to live joyfully with hope for the future.

Philippi

Thessalonica

Troas

Adriatic Sea

Aegean Sea

Paul, Silas, and Timothy headed for Thessalonica.

Thessalonica was a huge city and the capital of Macedonia.

WOW! 120,000 PEOPLE...

PHILIPPI WAS NOTHING COMPARED TO THIS....

LET'S FIND THE *JEWISH* COMMUNITY ...

MURMUR MURMUR MURMUR MURMUR

Once again, Paul and his companions found a Jewish synagogue and began speaking about Yeshua...

Several Jews and Greeks, some of high standing in the community, were baptized.

Acts 17:1-9 **177**

Acts 17:1-9

THE JEWS RALLIED SOME **TROUBLEMAKERS** TO START A **RIOT**! THEY'RE COMING HERE **NOW**!

WHAT?!

JUST LIKE WE SAID!

JASON, YOU'RE IN **DANGER**!!

SKRRCK!

IF I **RUN** WITH YOU, THEY'LL **CATCH** US ALL...

FLEX!

BUT IF I **STAY**, I CAN SLOW THEM DOWN...

BUT...!

DON'T DO ANYTHING STUPID!

PAUL AND THE OTHERS ESCAPED INTO THE NIGHT, BUT JASON...

YOU LET THEM **ESCAPE**...! YOU'LL **PAY** FOR THIS!!

HE WAS CAPTURED AND ACCUSED OF TREASON.

BUT WHEN THE COURTS COULD FIND NO EVIDENCE AGAINST HIM, HE WAS RELEASED.

NO... LET THEM GO!

JASON AND FRIENDS

HYUUUUU...

RABBI...

25. People of the Book

THIS IS SIMPLY *AMAZING...*

EVERYTHING YESHUA *DID* WAS FORETOLD...

YOU KNOW THE GREEKS ARE *ALSO* ACCEPTING THESE TEACHINGS ...

New Berean Believers

YOU'LL JUST HAVE TO *STAY* IN THE RIVER BAPTIZING... *ALL DAY, EVERY* DAY!

HA HA HA, BETTER NOT... I'LL CATCH A COLD...

RABBI! THOSE SAME JEWS FROM THESSALONICA HAVE *FOLLOWED* US HERE, AND THEY'VE STARTED ANOTHER *RIOT!*

THERE'S TROUBLE !!

!

26. The Unknown God

YAMMER

YAMMER

YAMMER

THERE YOU HAVE IT...

THE AREOPAGUS...

STILL FEEL LIKE TALKING?

WOW! THANK YOU!

THIS IS PERFECT!

GOOD PEOPLE OF ATHENS...!

IF PAUL WAS NERVOUS, HE DIDN'T SHOW IT...

THE TIME FOR **WORSHIPPING** STATUES MADE BY MAN HAS COME TO AN **END**. WE ALL CAN **SEEK** AND **KNOW** THE TRUE **GOD**...

THE FORMERLY **UNKNOWN** GOD OF THE **UNIVERSE!**

AND TO SHOW US HE WAS **CHOSEN**
:
GOD HAS **RAISED** HIM FROM THE **DEAD!**

GOD APPOINTED A MAN TO **REPRESENT** HIM TO THIS WORLD ...

RAISED FROM THE **DEAD**....?

HE'S **BLAS-PHEMING** APOLLO!!

GIVE US A BREAK!!

ALL AT ONCE, THE ATHENIANS STOPPED LISTENING...

BOOO

BOOO

IT FELT LIKE ANOTHER FRUITLESS EFFORT...

WAIT... SIR!

SIGH

Philippi

Thessalonica
Berea
Apollonia
Troas

Aegean Sea

Athens

Corinth

PAUL STAYED IN ATHENS THREE WEEKS...

THEN HE SAILED TO CORINTH.

27. Good News, Great Boldness

YAMMER

YAMMER

CORINTH HAS A **COOL** MARKET ...

NICE TENTS!

NEAT STITCHING...

PAUL WAS TRAINED AS A TENTMAKER FROM HIS YOUTH.

AHA... I SEE YOU HAVE AN **EYE** FOR QUALITY...

SHALOM! ARE YOU FROM JUDEA?

EVERY TRAVELER NEEDS A TENT... HOW ABOUT A **DISCOUNT?**

PRISCILLA
(WIFE OF TENTMAKER AQUILA)

ACTUALLY, I DON'T NEED A TENT...

...

PRISCILLA AND AQUILA WERE ROMAN JEWS WHO HAD BELIEVED IN YESHUA...

AFTER THE FESTIVAL OF WEEKS, THEY LEFT JERUSALEM AND RETURNED TO ROME...

●Rome

Corinth

BUT EMPEROR CLAUDIUS HATED JEWS AND FORCED THEM AND MANY OTHERS TO LEAVE.

CLAUDIUS

AQUILA AND PRISCILLA WERE HEARTBROKEN TO LEAVE THEIR ESTABLISHED LIFE IN ROME.

IT WAS OUR *HOME*...

IF ONLY WE'D HAD *CITIZENSHIP*, BUT...

...

sigh

SO PAUL SETTLED INTO LIFE IN CORINTH...

AND HE PREACHED IN THE SYNAGOGUE EVERY SABBATH...

WOBBLE WOBBLE

CAN YOU *TEACH* ME THAT STITCH?

PAUL WORKED WITH AQUILA AND THE OTHER TENTMAKERS TO COVER HIS EXPENSES.

A few weeks passed...

But as so many times before, the Jews ultimately turned against them.

They insulted Paul and cursed the name of Yeshua...

PAH
PAH
PAH

GLARE

YOUR BLOOD IS UPON YOUR OWN HEADS!

FROM NOW ON... I'LL GO TO THE **GENTILES!**

THIS BECAME AN IMPORTANT TURNING POINT IN THE COURSE OF PAUL'S MINISTRY...

HE WALKED OUT OF THE SYNAGOGUE...

AND INTO THE HOUSE NEXT DOOR WHERE HE BEGAN TEACHING.

JUSTUS

HMPH!

RABBI

I'VE WANTED TO MEET YOU...

MANY CAME TO JUSTUS'S HOUSE TO HEAR PAUL SPEAK...

AND HIS OPPONENTS DIDN'T LIKE THAT.

They brought Paul before Governor Gallio of Corinth...

THIS MAN'S TEACHING **OPPOSES** ROMAN LAW!

But Gallio found their complaints irritating...

THIS REGARDS YOUR **JEWISH** RELIGION! I'LL HAVE **NOTHING** TO DO WITH IT!

GET OUT OF MY COURTROOM!

AND HE DISMISSED THEM.

WHAT?! WHO **ORDERED** THIS TRIAL?!

THEY SEIZED SOSTHENES, THE JEW RESPONSIBLE FOR THE ARREST, AND BEAT HIM RIGHT THERE IN THE COURTROOM.

Paul stayed in Corinth another month until...

RABBI... WE SURE WILL **MISS** YOU...

HAVE A **SAFE** TRIP...

It was time to say farewell.

SEVERAL YOUNG GREEKS WHO ENJOYED WATCHING THE TRIALS WERE DISGUSTED BY THE POOR PROSECUTION...

SO LONG!

BYE!

PAUL LEFT FOR ANTIOCH, AND HE TOOK AQUILA AND PRISCILLA WITH HIM.

Letter to the Believers in Corinth

The city of Corinth became known for its wealth and corruption. And, the church in Corinth...

...SEEMED TO BE HEADING IN THE SAME DIRECTION.

IF THIS CONTINUES, OUR CHURCH WON'T SURVIVE...

WE NEED TO CONTACT PAUL!

IN ONE OF HIS LETTERS PAUL WROTE...

LOVE IS PATIENT, KIND...

WISH YOU WERE TALLER, DON'T YOU?

AND NOT JEALOUS.

LOOK AT MY MEDAL!

WOW!

LOVE IS NOT BOASTFUL OR PROUD.

HANG IN THERE!

I'VE GOT NOTHING.

YOU WILL BE OK!

LOVE'S NEVER IRRITABLE, IT KEEPS NO RECORD OF BEING WRONGED, AND IT REJOICES WHEN THE TRUTH WINS OUT.

Love never gives up, never loses faith, is always hopeful, and always endures.

IF I CAN HOLD ON JUST A LITTLE LONGER ...

LOVE WILL LAST FOREVER.

To the people of Corinth, Paul explained the powerful mystery of true love.

1 Corinthians 13

28. Strengthening the Disciples

Thessalonica

Troas

Berea

Aegean Sea

Ephesus

Athens

Corinth

THE COMPANY TRAVELED FIRST TO CENCHREA AND EPHESUS...

IN CENCHREA, PAUL TOOK A VOW AND SHAVED HIS HEAD...*

*This was a Jewish custom (See next page)

IN EPHESUS, PAUL ENTERED THE SYNAGOGUE ALONE...

AND PRESENTED THE WORD OF YESHUA TO THE JEWS THERE...

HMM...

WOULD YOU STAY A LITTLE **LONGER** TO TEACH US MORE?

I'M SORRY, BUT I **MUST** BE BACK IN JERUSALEM IN TIME FOR THE **FESTIVAL**...

Paul promised the people of Ephesus that he would return.

RABBI, YOUR IDEAS ARE **VERY** INTERESTING ⋮

Aquila and Priscilla, however...

RABBI, WE THINK MAYBE WE SHOULD **STAY** HERE.

THE PEOPLE OF EPHESUS ARE **EAGER** TO LEARN...

AND THE **SPIRIT** OF **GOD** IS **MOVING** HERE!

Antioch

Aegean Sea

Ephesus

Corinth

The Mediterranean Sea

Caesarea

Jerusalem

PAUL'S RETURN TO ANTIOCH MARKED THE END OF HIS SECOND MISSIONARY JOURNEY.

SO THE FRIENDS PARTED WAYS, AND PAUL CONTINUED TOWARD JERUSALEM.

THE NAZIRITE VOW

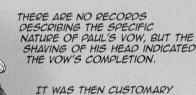

PAUL SHAVED HIS HEAD WHEN HE ARRIVED IN CENCHREA. THIS WAS A COMMON CUSTOM FOR THOSE TAKING A NAZIRITE VOW.

THERE ARE NO RECORDS DESCRIBING THE SPECIFIC NATURE OF PAUL'S VOW, BUT THE SHAVING OF HIS HEAD INDICATED THE VOW'S COMPLETION.

IT WAS THEN CUSTOMARY TO OFFER THE HAIR AT THE TEMPLE IN JERUSALEM, SO PAUL PROBABLY CONTINUED THERE FOR THIS PURPOSE.

29. A Teachable Genius

PREPARE TO RECEIVE THE *WORD* OF THE LORD!

AHH!

EPHESUS!

AFTER A LONG JOURNEY FROM *ALEXANDRIA**, YOU'RE A *BEAUTIFUL* SIGHT!

APOLLOS

* Alexandria: a city in Egypt

APOLLOS WAS A TEACHER OF GOD'S WORD WHO ARRIVED IN EPHESUS JUST AFTER PAUL LEFT...

HE WAS A GIFTED SPEAKER, HANDSOME...

AND THE PEOPLE IN THE SYNAGOGUE ENJOYED LISTENING TO HIM...

I TELL YOU, THIS IS NOT A GAME! THE KINGDOM OF GOD IS NEAR!

TURN FROM YOUR OLD WAYS AND BELIEVE GOD!

PREPARE FOR THE COMING MESSIAH...

RECEIVE THE BAPTISM OF JOHN!

...

...

I WANT TO CHANGE!!!

BAPTIZE ME!

AND ME!

YES, I AGREE...

Aquila and Priscilla invited Apollos to their house...

THAT MEETING OPENED APOLLOS'S EYES TO THE POWER OF GOD'S WORK THROUGH YESHUA.

Meanwhile...

WHEN AQUILA AND PRISCILLA TOLD APOLLOS ABOUT THE NEEDS IN CORINTH, HE DECIDED TO GO. HE BECAME SO INFLUENTIAL IN THE CHURCH THERE THAT A DISPUTE AROSE REGARDING WHETHER HE OR PAUL SHOULD BE MORE HIGHLY REGARDED.

After only a short time in Antioch...

Paul departed again for what would be his third missionary journey.

30. The Third Wave and Beyond

Iconium

Antioch of Pisidia
Lystra Derbe Tarsus Antioch

Ephesus

Corinth

While Apollos taught in Corinth, Paul traveled by land on his way to Ephesus.

RABBI!

WELCOME!!

HUG

There was a happy reunion in Ephesus, but...

YAAAY!!

YAAAY!

... HOLY SPIRIT? WHAT'S THAT?

WELL... WE DID RECEIVE JOHN'S BAPTISM FROM APOLLOS.

JOHN ...?

JOHN THE BAP-TIZER?

WE'VE BEEN REPENTING TO GET READY FOR MESSIAH TO COME ...

YESHUA, THE **MESSIAH**, HAS ALREADY COME AND FORGIVEN OUR SINS BY DYING ON THE **CROSS**...

JOHN THE BAPTIZER DIED 25 **YEARS** AGO!

HE TAUGHT US TO BELIEVE IN **YESHUA**, THE ONE COMING **AFTER** HIM!

OH!

TWELVE YOUNG PEOPLE WERE BAPTIZED THAT DAY IN THE NAME OF YESHUA...

AND WHEN PAUL LAID HIS HANDS ON THEM, THEY WERE FILLED WITH THE HOLY SPIRIT.

PAUL TAUGHT IN EPHESUS FOR THREE MONTHS...

THE PEOPLE LISTENED EAGERLY AT FIRST...

HMPH!

BUT THINGS CHANGED...

WHAT HAVE I **GOTTEN** MYSELF **INTO?**

Some of the Jews became hostile and forced Paul to leave the synagogue...

IT'S **EASY** TO WALK **OUT** OF THE SYNAGOGUE...

BUT NOW I'M LEFT WITH NOWHERE TO TEACH!

!

EXCUSE ME, **RABBI**...!

I'M TYRAN-NUS.

I HAVE A **LECTURE HALL** YOU COULD USE IF YOU LIKE...

HUH?

So Paul taught every day in Tyrannus's lecture hall...

People came from all over Asia to study and then went out to start new churches in other cities.

WOOOOOW!!

GOD'S WORKING POWERFULLY HERE!

HE HEALED SOMEONE TWO DAYS AGO...

HE CAN DO *ANYTHING* IN YESHUA'S NAME...

HE DROVE THAT EVIL SPIRIT OUT!

HMM...

IF *HIM*... WHY NOT US?

THIS IS *OUR* AREA OF EXPERTISE, AFTER ALL...

IF USING THIS FELLOW'S *NAME* IS AS EASY AS THEY *SAY* IT IS...

THERE'S PROFIT POTENTIAL HERE!

SONS OF SCEVA
(TRAVELING EXORCISTS)

HE'S TORMENTED BY A SPIRIT ... I'LL PAY ANY PRICE!

YARRGH!

DOCTORS, PLEASE! MY HUSBAND *NEEDS* HELP...

THIS IS OUR SPECIALTY...

SMIRK!

AT YOUR SERVICE, MA'AM...

DON'T WORRY!

Acts 19:1-41 **211**

OUCH!

GUR...K

HEEELP!

The seven sons of Sceva, a leading priest...

Were beaten badly by the power of the demon in the possessed man.

GULP!

AWAWAWA

Those who saw the spectacle were amazed...

And told the story throughout Ephesus.

WOW! THIS POWER FROM GOD IS *SERIOUS* !!

MANY QUIT DABBLING IN WITCHCRAFT...

IF I *TRULY* BELIEVE IN GOD, HOW CAN I USE MAGIC ANY *LONGER*...?

I'M TURNING BACK TO GOD!

SHAAA...

THESE *CHARMS* NEVER HELPED ME, ANYWAY...

At that time, the Ephesians commonly used witchcraft and spells to worship their goddess Artemis. People came from all over Ephesus with their items of witchcraft...

The books, scrolls, and charms burned were worth around 50,000 drachmas, or several million dollars.

I CAME HERE 2 1/2 *YEARS* AGO...

A *LOT* HAS *HAPPENED* SINCE THEN...

THERE ARE *MANY* DISCIPLES NOW, AND THEY HAVE *SPREAD* THE WORK OF YESHUA *ABROAD*, AS WELL...

IT *MIGHT* BE TIME TO MOVE ON :

Once again, Paul began making plans...

FLUTTER FLUTTER CHIRP CHIRP

TIM-OTHY!

ERASTUS!

YOU TWO WILL GO TO **MACEDONIA** AND **ACHAIA**...

YES?

TIMOTHY

ERASTUS WAS ONE OF PAUL'S DISCIPLES...

TITUS!

OK!

ERASTUS

TITUS

I'D LIKE *YOU* TO GO TO CORINTH. *CHECK* ON THE BELIEVERS THERE, AND BRING ME A *REPORT*.

YES, RABBI!

CORINTHIAN LIFESTYLES HAD BECOME NOTORIOUSLY SHAMELESS IN THOSE TIMES...

IN A LETTER, PAUL URGED THE BELIEVERS NOT TO EVEN SOCIALIZE WITH IMMORAL PEOPLE WHO CLAIMED TO FOLLOW YESHUA.

SO PAUL'S ASSISTANTS LEFT FOR VARIOUS CITIES, AND PAUL PREPARED TO DEPART ON HIS OWN...

HOWEVER...

Letter to the Believers in Ephesus

Ephesus was an important port town between the Mediterranean and Black seas.

In his letter, Paul explained how everything changed for Jews after the coming of Yeshua.

...THAT LEAD TO **DEATH!**

TILL NOW, YOU'VE BEEN **LIVING** LIVES...

DESTRUCTION

AFTER ALL MY **MISTAKES**, THERE'S NO HOPE LEFT.

BUT I **DIED** TO PAY FOR **YOUR** MISTAKES.

BUT GOD RESCUED US BY SENDING YESHUA...

IT'S **NEVER** TOO LATE TO START AGAIN, AND I WILL **LEAD** YOU.

Stand up...

A **NEW** LIFE...

I CAN HAVE A NEW **LIFE.**

So Paul encouraged the believers to speak the truth in love and to grow more and more like Yeshua, who is the head of his body, the church.

PAUL DESCRIBED THE CHURCH BY COMPARING IT TO YESHUA'S BODY.

ALL BELIEVERS ARE UNITED IN YESHUA, WORKING AND GROWING TOGETHER.

HE'S THE HEAD!

WE'RE HANDS...

LEGS!

WE ARE **MANY** PARTS, AND TOGETHER WE MAKE THE **CHURCH!**

THE CHURCH

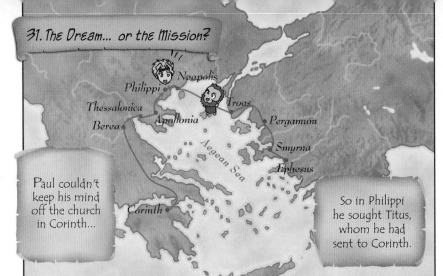

31. The Dream... or the Mission?

Neapolis
Philippi
Troas
Thessalonica
Apollonia
Berea
Pergamum
Aegean Sea
Smyrna
Ephesus
Corinth

Paul couldn't keep his mind off the church in Corinth...

So in Philippi he sought Titus, whom he had sent to Corinth.

RABBI!

TITUS! LUKE! LYDIA!!

RABBI, YOU WON'T **BELIEVE** IT! YOUR LETTERS HAVE MADE AN **IMPACT**, AND THE CHURCH HAS BEEN **REPENTING**!

IS **THAT** RIGHT ?!

SO MANY **PEOPLE** HAVE BEEN **CHANGING**... IT'S **AMAZING**!

PAUL WAS SO INSPIRED, HE DECIDED TO WRITE ANOTHER LETTER IMMEDIATELY.

DEAR BROTHERS AND SISTERS IN CORINTH...

IN HIS LETTER, PAUL ASKED THE BELIEVERS IN CORINTH TO TAKE AN OFFERING FOR THE POOR IN THE JERUSALEM CHURCH.

TITUS, TAKE THIS LETTER TO THE **BELIEVERS** IN CORINTH...

IT'S MY **DREAM** TO TRAVEL TO SPAIN BY WAY OF ROME AND **SHARE** THE GOOD NEWS THERE...

BUT FIRST, IT'S MY **MISSION** TO PRESENT THIS OFFERING IN **JERUSALEM**!

I'LL SEE YOU IN **CORINTH** THEN...

Philippi

Amphipolis

Thessalonica

Apollonia

Berea

Corinth

SO TITUS WENT AHEAD AND PAUL VISITED THE BELIEVERS IN MACEDONIA ON HIS WAY TO CORINTH.

CORINTH

I'M HERE **ONLY** BRIEFLY BECAUSE I'M ON MY WAY TO **ROME**...

TIMOTHY, TERTIUS, CAN YOU **WRITE** FOR ME?

...IN FACT, I'D LIKE TO **WRITE** THEM WHILE I'M **HERE**...

SURE!

RABBI... MAY WE **LISTEN** WHILE YOU DICTATE?

OF **COURSE!** THAT'S FINE!

And so it was here in Corinth that Paul composed his historic letter to the believers in Rome.

SCRCH

SCRCHH

Letter to the Believers in Rome

Paul's letter to the church in Rome was full of spiritual insight and power.

One of the first themes of this letter was the importance of a believer's faith...

I'M **NOT** ASHAMED OF THIS GOOD NEWS!

IT'S THE **POWER** OF GOD ...

FIRST FOR THE JEWS, BUT NOW FOR **EVERYONE** WHO BELIEVES!

Paul showed how Yeshua's work and teachings fulfilled the prophecies of the Ancient Texts.

LOOKS LIKE WE'RE THE ONLY ONES WHO'LL BE GOING TO HEAVEN!

In those days, it was understood that only the most honorable Jews would be saved...

But Paul explained that no one can be saved by being good...

EVEN THOUGH WE'RE **NOT** JEWS, WE CAN BELIEVE AND BE **SAVED?**

God chose to save the world through the Jews, and now that Yeshua has come, all people can be saved through belief in him.

The second theme in Paul's letter explores the challenges of becoming a new person.

BAD WAY

GOOD WAY

WHY IS THIS SO *DIFFICULT?*

GOOD

EVIL

I *KNOW* THE WAY I *WANT* TO GO...

BUT I GO THE WAY I *DON'T* WANT TO GO!

I *WANT* TO GO THIS WAY...

BUT I GO *THIS* WAY INSTEAD!

OH! *WHAT* CAN I DO?

HEY!

BUT IT'S NO LONGER *I* WHO DO WRONG, BUT THE *SIN* LIVING IN ME.

BUT THIS *NEW* LIFE TELLS US TO DO WHAT'S *RIGHT!*

NEW LIFE

OLD NATURE

AND THOUGH IT *TORMENTS* ME...

SHING!

AHH!

PAUL, DON'T WORRY ANY LONGER...

I AM YOUR *MASTER* NOW.

YESHUA!!

OH... SO THE BATTLE IS *OVER!*

YESHUA ALREADY *TOOK* MY PUNISHMENT!

I GUESS I'LL JUST *TRUST* HIM...

AND *OBEY* THE HOLY SPIRIT!

Paul encouraged his readers to believe that their sins were forgiven and that they had received a new nature in Yeshua.

Book of Romans

Finally, Paul wrote of the future glory believers can look forward to.

THIS **BODY** WILL ONE DAY BE GONE...

AND THIS EARTH AS WELL...

ALL THAT WE SEE AND TOUCH WILL ONE DAY BE DESTROYED...

AND EVERYTHING WILL BE MADE NEW.

I'M **NOT** DEAD?

MY DAUGHTER!!

!!

!!

GRANDPA?!!

The children of God will be raised again.

SO I **DON'T** NEED TO BE AFRAID OF DEATH... YESHUA!

Book of Romans

These things will happen when Jerusalem is reconciled...

I WILL LIVE BY LISTENING TO YOU, GOD.

So offer your bodies to God, as living sacrifices, holy and pleasing to him.

Three months later...

GOOD! LET'S GET **GOING!** I WANT TO SAIL OUT OF **CENCHREA!**

HERE'S THE **OFFERING,** RABBI...

SHWIP

RABBI! WAIT!!

!

DAH TAH

DAH TAH

WHOA...

WHAT'S **WRONG** ?

YOU **CAN'T SAIL** FROM **CENCHREA** !!

HUF

HUF

WE JUST LEARNED OF A **PLOT** TO TRAP YOU AND **KILL** YOU ON THE **VOYAGE!**

WHAT?!

Philippi

Berea

Corinth

BUT THE ROUTE THROUGH **MACEDONIA** SHOULD BE **SAFE!**

BUT THEN WE CAN'T REACH **JERUSALEM** IN TIME FOR THE **PASSOVER** ...

BUT I **SUPPOSE** THERE'S NO OTHER WAY...

Paul reluctantly changed his plans and hoped to reach Jerusalem in time for the Festival of Weeks.

Philippi

Troas

SO PAUL TRAVELED TO PHILIPPI AND BOARDED A SHIP THERE FOR TROAS.

Corinth

ALONG THE WAY, HE WAS JOINED BY GENTILE BELIEVERS WHO WANTED TO HELP HIM PRESENT THE GIFT OFFERING TO JERUSALEM.

SOPATER, SON OF PYRRHUS, JOINED FROM BEREA...

ARISTAR-CHUS AND SECUNDUS FROM THESSA-LONICA...

GAIUS AND TIMOTHY FROM LYCAONIA...

AND TITUS REPRESENTING THE CHURCH IN CORINTH.

LUKE JOINED THE GROUP AS WELL...

AHHH! THE FRESH SCENT OF A JOURNEY!

The party stayed in Troas for a week. On the last night, a curious incident occurred...

Paul was speaking to the group about the Lord's Supper when...

ZZH ZZH

ZZZZZZZZZ

WHA- NOOO!!

EUTYCHUS JUST FELL **THREE** STORIES!

WHAT HAPPENED?!

EUTY- CHUUUS!!

DOCTOR LUKE, IS HE... OK?

ARRGGGH! N-NO... I'M I'M AFRAID HE'S NOT...

NO PULSE...

WOWWWWW!!

What looked like an evening of disaster ended in amazement.

HOW'S THAT **POSSIBLE** ??

Thessalonica • Apollonia • Troas • Assos • Berea • Aegean Sea • Ephesus • Miletus

Paul departed Troas for Miletus...

I'D **LIKE** TO STOP IN EPHESUS, BUT THERE'S **NO** TIME...

KRACKLE

KRACKLE

So Paul called the Ephesian elders to Miletus...

RABBI !!

!!

MY **FRIENDS**... THIS IS THE **LAST** TIME YOU WILL EVER SEE ME...

SO I MUST **WARN** YOU...

WHEN I'M **GONE**, FALSE TEACHERS WILL **ATTACK** YOUR PEOPLE LIKE **SAVAGE** WOLVES...

AS LEADERS...

YOU MUST KEEP A **CAREFUL** WATCH!

NEVER FORGET THE **YEARS** WE'VE SPENT TOGETHER...

NEVER FORGET MY **TEARS** FOR YOUR STRENGTH AND FOR YOUR **SAFETY**...

AS THE **LORD** HAS SAID...

IT IS A **BETTER** REWARD TO **GIVE** THAN TO RECEIVE...

SO I'VE **NEVER** ASKED FOR OR **WANTED** YOUR GOLD OR SILVER!

I LIVED **SIMPLY** BECAUSE I WANTED TO ENCOURAGE **YOU** TO THINK OF OTHERS BEFORE YOURSELVES, AND TO **HELP** THE POOR AND THE NEEDY...

BUT— BUT RABBI!!

When Paul told the elders they would not see him again, they wept.

...

THEY EMBRACED MANY TIMES BEFORE WATCHING AS HE SAILED FROM THE HARBOR.

PAUL STOPPED IN TYRE, PTOLEMAIS...

...AND CAESAREA.

Troas
Assos
Ephesus
Miletus
Patara
Tyre
Ptolemais
Caesarea
Jerusalem

CAESAREA

BUT... I MUST *COMPLETE* MY TASK!

RABBI ...?

AHHH...

WHEREVER I GO, THE HOLY SPIRIT *SPEAKS* TO ME OF THE *DIFFICULTIES* AHEAD...

HELLO! ARE YOU PAUL?

PHILIP! I'VE **HEARD** SO MUCH ABOUT YOUR **WORK** HERE!!

GOOD TO **MEET** YOU, SIR ...

WE'VE BEEN **EXPECTING** YOU...

MY NAME IS **PHILIP!**

Do you remember Philip? He was one of those chosen to oversee food distribution in the early days, when the church in Jerusalem was still young. (See p. 51.)

RABBI... PLEASE COME **REST**... YOU'VE HAD A **LONG** JOURNEY!

32. Truth Worth Dying For

I HOPE YOU CAN **RELAX** WITH US BEFORE YOUR TRIP TO **JERUSALEM** ...

THANK YOU, **PHILIP** ...

LET ME INTRODUCE YOU TO MY **DAUGHTERS**... WHO ALL HAVE THE GIFT OF **PROPHECY** ...

WE'VE ALL BEEN **HOPING** TO HEAR THE STORIES OF YOUR **JOURNEYS**...

AHA! WE'D BETTER GET **STARTED** THEN, OR I'LL HAVE TO BE HERE FOR A **WEEK!**

PAUL DIDN'T KNOW THAT NOT FAR AWAY, SOMEONE WAS LOOKING FOR HIM, ANOTHER PERSON WITH THE PROPHETIC GIFT WHOSE NAME WAS **AGABUS**.

HE HAD TRAVELED FROM **JERUSALEM** TO **CAESAREA**...

...TO DELIVER A MESSAGE.

IT'S A **PRIVILEGE** TO HAVE MET HIM...

PLEASE LET US **PRAY** FOR YOU, RABBI...

...AND MAY YOUR WILL, OH LORD, BE DONE...

...AMEN!

PHILIP...

EVERYONE...

I DON'T KNOW **HOW** TO THANK YOU...

Leaving Caesarea, Paul remembered his Lord, Yeshua, who had also made a final trip to Jerusalem...

Knowing that there he would be crucified.

33. Gathering Clouds

Some of the believers from Caesarea had joined Paul for the journey...

WELCOME, RABBI!!

They brought him to the home of Mnason of Cyprus.

The next day they visited James, the brother of Yeshua, with the offering from the Gentiles.

AS LEADER OF THE CHURCH IN JERUSALEM...

JAMES ACCEPTED THE GIFT FROM THE GENTILE BROTHERS AND SISTERS.

Paul began to share about their travels...

And the believers rejoiced at the news of God's work among the Gentiles.

BUT RABBI, THERE IS ONE PROBLEM...

PROBLEM?

THERE'S A RUMOR HERE IN JERUSALEM...

THAT YOU REJECT MOSES...

AND FORBID THE CIRCUMCISION OF CHILDREN...

!?!

DIDN'T WE ALL **AGREE** AT THE CONFERENCE ⋮ **JEWISH** BELIEVERS SHOULD **KEEP** THEIR CUSTOMS...

BUT THE **GENTILES** SHOULDN'T BE **REQUIRED** TO DO SO?!

OF COURSE WE DON'T **FORCE** THE GENTILES TO FOLLOW OUR CUSTOMS...!

BUT AMONG THE **JEWS** WHO HAVE BELIEVED IN **YESHUA**... THERE ARE MANY WHO **STILL** FEEL IT'S IMPORTANT TO **KEEP** THE JEWISH TRADITIONS.

RABBI... MAY I OFFER AN **IDEA**...?

...

James recommended that Paul take a sacred vow in the Jewish tradition...

TOMORROW WOULD BE A **GOOD** DAY FOR IT... FOUR OTHERS WILL **ALSO** BE COMPLETING VOWS ...

GREAT IDEA! THEN THEY'LL **SEE** THAT I KEEP THE LAW AND **AGREE** WITH THEM!

. . .

AND THE *REST* OF YOU...

DON'T WORRY!

BUT FOR THE SAKE OF THE *JEWISH* BELIEVERS ...

PLEASE DON'T EAT *BLOOD*, OR FOOD SACRIFICED TO *IDOLS* ...

NO MEAT OF STRANGLED *ANIMALS*,

NO SEXUAL *IMMORALITY*...

AND YOU'LL BE *FINE!*

Phew!

Ugh!

?

VICTIM

YOU *DON'T* WANT TO BE CIRCUMCISED AS AN ADULT! *TRUST ME!*

THE NEXT DAY, PAUL WENT TO THE TEMPLE, AS PLANNED.

THE CEREMONY LASTED SEVEN DAYS...

ON THE LAST DAY, PARTICIPANTS HAD THEIR HEADS SHAVED AT THE TEMPLE...

EVERYONE FELT THIS WAS AN EXCELLENT WAY TO DEFUSE ANY POTENTIAL HOSTILITY. HOWEVER...

AND ON **TOP** OF THAT...

MURMUR MURMUR

!!

HE'S BROUGHT **FOREIGNERS** INTO THE HOLY **TEMPLE!**

ACTUALLY... I **DID** SEE THAT GUY WITH SOME **GREEKS** JUST THIS MORNING...

GET HIM OUT OF THE TEMPLE...!

GRUMBLE

GRUMBLE

GRAB HIM!

Some of the Jews who had opposed Paul in Ephesus happened to be at the Temple that day...

YAAAAH!

When they spotted Paul, they threw the town into an uproar.

The Roman military arrived shortly to restore order...

WHAT'S GOING ON HERE?!

They grabbed Paul and bound him with chains.

I CAN'T **BELIEVE** I ALMOST FLOGGED A **ROMAN** CITIZEN!

SHUDDER

There were severe penalties for punishing any Roman citizen without a trial.

CITIZENS WERE TO BE GIVEN A TRIAL...

SO THE COMMANDER BROUGHT PAUL TO THE JEWISH HIGH COUNCIL.

I'VE DONE MY **DUTY** BEFORE GOD AND MEN...

I HAVE **NOTHING** TO HIDE ...

HE **DARES** CALL HIMSELF **RELIGIOUS** !!!

HMPH!

STRIKE HIM IN THE **MOUTH!**

!

GLARE

GOD WILL STRIKE YOU... **HYPOCRITE** !!!

Immediately, an argument broke out within the council...

NO ONE RETURNS FROM THE DEAD!

But the Pharisees did.

EZEKIEL'S PROPHECY!

The Sadducees didn't believe in angels or an afterlife...

HE'S A FOOL!

THE TEXTS SAY HE'S RIGHT!

YOU CAN'T CONVICT THIS MAN!

A SPIRIT MAY HAVE SPOKEN TO HIM!

HE'S A LIAR!

HE'S GUILTY OF BLASPHEMY!

...

THIS HAS GOT TO STOP...

MEN!

I WANT PAUL OUT OF HERE!

FOR ME TO THE PEOPLE OF JERUSALEM...

JUST AS YOU HAVE SPOKEN

LORD...

YOU WILL SPEAK TO THE PEOPLE OF ROME!

...

MY LORD...

PLEASE DON'T ALLOW IT!

THERE WILL BE 40 PEOPLE WAITING TO AMBUSH HIM!

ALL RIGHT, I *WON'T* PERMIT IT....

BUT *KEEP* THIS TO YOURSELF, *UNDERSTAND?*

HEY! LISTEN UP!

!

YOU'RE *LEAVING* FOR CAESAREA AT 9 O'CLOCK *TONIGHT!*

I WANT 200 SOLDIERS, 200 SPEARMEN, AND 70 MOUNTED TROOPS!

AND BRING A HORSE FOR *PAUL*... I WANT HIM DELIVERED TO CAESAREA *SAFELY!*

YES SIR!

SO PAUL WAS TAKEN TO CAESAREA...

TROMP

TROMP

TROMP

TROMP

TROMP

...WITH AN ENTIRE ARMY TO ESCORT HIM.

CAESAREA

MY LORD.... A LETTER FROM COMMANDER *LYSIAS*....

...

HMM?

FELIX
(GOVERNOR OF JUDEA)

"FROM CLAUDIUS LYSIAS, TO HIS EXCELLENCY, GOVERNOR FELIX: GREETINGS!

"MY TROOPS RESCUED THIS MAN BEFORE HE WAS KILLED BY JEWISH RIOTERS IN JERUSALEM...

"HIS NAME IS PAUL, AND HE IS A LEGAL ROMAN CITIZEN."

"I HAVE REVIEWED HIS CASE AND FOUND THAT THE ACCUSATIONS AGAINST HIM PERTAIN TO HIS JEWISH RELIGION..."

But the man has not committed any crime requiring imprisonment or punishment. I told his accusers to present their case before you.

HMM...

OKAY, YOU'RE A ROMAN *CITIZEN*?

YES.

WHERE ARE YOU *FROM*?

I'M FROM CILICIA.

HMM...

I'LL *HEAR* YOUR CASE MYSELF WHEN YOUR *ACCUSERS* ARRIVE!

UNTIL THEN... KEEP HIM UNDER *GUARD* IN THE PALACE!

Acts 23:12-35   **257**

Five days later, the high priest, Ananias, arrived with several elders and a lawyer.

HE'S A LEADER OF A NAZARENE **CULT** THAT STIRS UP OPPOSITION TO THE **ROMAN** GOVERNMENT.

SIR, THIS **MAN** IS A TROUBLEMAKER OF THE **WORST** SORT...

A FEW DAYS AGO, HE TRIED TO **DESECRATE** OUR HOLY TEMPLE...

WHEN WE CAPTURED HIM, THE **COMMANDER** SEIZED HIM...

AND DIDN'T ALLOW US TO ADMINISTER **JUSTICE**!

TERTULLUS
(LAWYER)

...

...

CLEARLY WE ARE PLACED IN A **DIFFICULT** POSITION ...

Felix listened carefully to Tertullus's finely crafted argument...

YOU MAY SPEAK, PAUL...

SIR, TO MAKE MY **DEFENSE** BEFORE YOU...

IS A **PLEASURE**...

FOR I **KNOW** YOU HAVE PRESIDED OVER JEWISH AFFAIRS FOR **MANY** YEARS!

SMILE

I SEE...

With clarity and composure, Paul presented his defense to the governor...

AND THERE IS **ABSOLUTELY** NO EVIDENCE TO **SUGGEST** THAT I HAVE!

IT WAS ONLY **TWELVE** DAYS AGO THAT I RETURNED TO **JERUSALEM**...

I HAVE **NEVER** INCITED A RIOT OR CREATED A **DISTURBANCE** OF ANY SORT...

BUT I **BELIEVE** IN THE GOD OF MY ANCESTORS AND THE WAY OF **SALVATION** :

AND MY **ACCUSERS** DON'T **AGREE** WITH MY BELIEFS!

AFTER **TRAVELING** FOR SEVERAL YEARS, I **RETURNED** TO JERUSALEM AND...

ARGH! HMPH!

I WENT TO THE TEMPLE TO PRESENT AN **OFFERING** TO GOD ...

FIRST MY HEAD WAS **SHAVED**, IN ACCORDANCE WITH **JEWISH** CUSTOM...

THEN MY **ACCUSERS** SAW ME PRESENTING MY OFFERING AND **DRAGGED** ME AWAY!

Paul went on to explain that it was the Jews from Ephesus who created this uproar...

And how in the council, Paul had only said he believed in the resurrection of the dead...

Felix believed Paul and felt confident of his innocence...

But hoping Paul would give him a bribe, he postponed the trial...

ANANIAS, *WAIT* FOR ME TO CALL *YOU!*

So Paul remained a prisoner in Caesarea, but was granted freedom to meet with friends regularly...

Many believers visited Paul and brought him food...

AND EVEN GOVERNOR FELIX...

THIS PAUL'S AN INTERESTING FELLOW...

VISITED SEVERAL TIMES WITH HIS JEWISH WIFE, DRUSILLA, TO LISTEN TO PAUL'S TEACHINGS. BUT THERE WAS LITTLE EVIDENCE THAT HE WANTED ANYTHING MORE THAN MONEY.

Two years later...

SHWOOOOOO...

FELIX HAD LEFT PAUL IN PRISON FOR TWO YEARS BECAUSE HE DIDN'T WANT TO OFFEND THE JEWS...

SIGHHHH...

BUT THEN...

POM ♪ POPPA ♪ POMMMM ♫

HURRAH!

LONG LIVE GOVERNOR FESTUS!

...

LONG LIVE OUR NEW GOVERNOR !!!

LONG LIVE FESTUS!

GOVERNOR FESTUS

34. Defending the Truth

FESTUS RETURNED TO CAESAREA AND IMMEDIATELY REOPENED THE TRIAL.

DMM DMM DMM DMM

BOOO

YOU'RE A DISGRACE TO YOUR PEOPLE!

AND A TRAITOR TO ROME!

BOOO

BOOO

BOOO

KILL HIM!

FLOG HIM!

BOOO

HE'S A CRIMINAL!!

Paul was accused of several serious crimes...

BOOO BOOO BOOO

But the Jewish leaders had no proof to back up their accusations.

And Paul's defense...

I AM... INNOCENT!

I'VE BROKEN **NO** JEWISH LAWS...

I'VE **NEVER** VIOLATED THE TEMPLE ...

I'VE NEVER **OPPOSED** ROME!

His defense was simple and his innocence apparent.

HMM... I HAVE NO **EVIDENCE** TO SUGGEST THIS MAN IS **GUILTY**...

BUT THE JEWISH LEADERS WILL **HATE** ME IF I SET HIM FREE...

IT'S ALL IN REGARD TO THEIR RELIGIOUS BELIEFS...

I THINK CAESAREA IS THE **WRONG** PLACE TO HOLD **THIS** TRIAL!

...

I'VE DECIDED TO MOVE IT TO **JERUSALEM**! ...

YOU HAVE **NO** RIGHT TO TURN ME OVER TO **THESE MEN!**

FOR **THAT** WILL SENTENCE ME TO **DEATH!!**

WHAT?!

THEREFORE, AS A ROMAN CITIZEN...

I APPEAL TO CAESAR!

I MUST BE TRIED IN ROME BEFORE **CAESAR !!!**

HA HA HA... **FINE!**

YOU HAVE **APPEALED** TO CAESAR, AND TO **CAESAR** YOU'LL GO!

BUT THAT'S NOT FAIR!!!

Festus was glad to be relieved of what seemed a sinister case.

WHILE PAUL AWAITED HIS TRANSFER TO ROME...

SWSSH

AN UNEXPECTED VISITOR ARRIVED IN CAESAREA...

WHEW!!

IT'S A GOOD DEAL **COOLER** HERE THAN IN **MY** COUNTRY...

KING AGRIPPA II

THE KING, WHO HAD VISITED, TO HONOR THE NEW GOVERNOR, BECAME INTRIGUED BY PAUL'S CASE...

SO I'M **GLAD** TO BE RID OF HIM, REALLY...

BUT NOW I MUST **EXPLAIN** THIS MESS TO THE **EMPEROR**, YOU SEE...

HMM... I'M **FAMILIAR** WITH JEWISH LAW, WHY DON'T YOU LET ME **HELP** YOU?

...

...

So PAUL WAS CALLED BEFORE KING AGRIPPA, AND HE BEGAN BY TELLING HIM HOW HE HAD PERSECUTED FOLLOWERS OF THE WAY...

THEN HOW HE MET YESHUA ON THE ROAD TO DAMASCUS...

AND OF ALL HIS JOURNEYS AND EXPERIENCES FROM THAT DAY ON...

HE APPEARS **INNOCENT**, DOESN'T HE?

...

YES...

IF HE HADN'T APPEALED TO **CAESAR**, HE COULD GO **FREE**...

ROME WILL BE **TOUGH** ON HIM...

SWSSH

YES.

And so Paul awaited his transfer to Rome.

35. Great Trials, Greater Opportunities

Winter was approaching when Paul and a troop of soldiers began the long voyage to Rome.

Mura

Rhodes

Sidon

Caesarea

Jerusalem

Phoenix

Crete

Fair Haven

Bad weather made the first several weeks difficult...

CRETE

HYUOUUUU...

THIS WINTER **WIND**...

IT SEEMS TO BE GETTING **STRONGER**...

The storm continued for days, blotting out the stars and the sun...

No one had eaten any food in a long time...

RABBI...

IS THERE ANY HOPE?

...

MEN... I *WARNED* YOU...

HAD YOU *LISTENED*... NONE OF THIS WOULD HAVE *HAPPENED!*

Ooo!

UUhh

...

BUT NOW TAKE *HEART!*

THIS SHIP WILL BE *DESTROYED,* BUT EVERYONE WILL LIVE...

AN *ANGEL* STOOD BESIDE ME LAST NIGHT...

HE TOLD ME WE WOULD RUN *AGROUND* ON AN ISLAND.

YES, CAPTAIN... IT'S *TRUE.*

IS– IS IT *TRUE,* PAUL...?

The ship grounded in Malta and was destroyed on the rocks, but all 276 on board made it safely to shore.

PAUL, SIR... IT'S ALL MY *FAULT* !!

PLEASE FORGIVE ME!!

OVER THERE!

STOP!

When the ship began to sink, the soldiers prepared to kill the prisoners so that none would escape...

NO!!

But Lieutenant Julius stopped them...

STAND BACK!!

So Paul and the other prisoners were allowed to live.

PAUL... SIR... ARE YOU OK?

...

YES, THANK YOU.

EEHH... HE MUST HAVE BEEN A MURDERER!

HE **SURVIVED** THE SEA, BUT THE GODS OF **JUSTICE** STILL CAUGHT HIM...

AYIY!!

RABBI! SHAKE IT **OFF**!

GASP

!

OH! NO!

WHISPER

SCARY!

WHISPER

HE'LL BE DEAD WITHIN **MINUTES** ...

AHH! IT'S ALL RIGHT!

WHAT?!

SHHAAK!

A VIPER JUST BIT YOU!!!

WA HA HA HA HA HA

Hours later, Paul still appeared to be fine...

Many rumors circulated about Paul after that.

HE MUST BE A **GOD**!

WHISPER

?!

THAT GUY'S STILL ALIVE?!

WHISPER

WOW!

WHISPER

For three months, Paul and the others wintered on the island...

And Paul stayed busy...

THE ISLAND'S CHIEF OFFICIAL HAD A FATHER SUFFERING FROM DYSENTERY...

...AND PAUL HEALED HIM.

AFTER THAT, SICK PEOPLE FROM ALL OVER THE ISLAND CAME TO PAUL, AND HE HEALED THEM ALL.

RABBI!

PAUL, SIR... **THANK** YOU!

THANK YOU!

YOURS IS THE **GREAT** GOD...

PRAISE PAUL'S GOD!

PRAISE GOD!

THE ISLANDERS ADMIRED PAUL DEEPLY, AND WHEN IT WAS TIME FOR HIM TO LEAVE...

THEY HONORED HIM WITH GIFTS AND THE SUPPLIES HE AND THE CREW NEEDED FOR THE REST OF THEIR JOURNEY.

Adriatic Sea

Puteoli

Rhegium

Crete

Syracuse

Malta

Finally, the travelers arrived in Puteoli.

Paul was encouraged by the welcome he received from the believers in Rome...

And although he was carefully monitored by the Roman guard...

HE WAS ALLOWED TO CHOOSE WHERE HE WANTED TO LIVE.

So Paul's house became a destination for people from all over Italy...

Where the great rabbi could be found teaching the message of Yeshua.

"FIVE TIMES I RECEIVED THE 39 LASHES OF THE JEWS...

"THREE TIMES I WAS BEATEN BY THE RODS OF THE ROMANS...

"I WAS STONED...

"THREE TIMES SHIPWRECKED!

"ONCE I SPENT A WHOLE DAY AND NIGHT ADRIFT AT SEA...

"I HAVE FACED DANGERS FROM RIVERS, FROM ROBBERS, AND FROM THE HANDS OF MY OWN PEOPLE...

The Ancient Texts don't detail any more of Paul's experiences. But other sources indicate that Paul's dream came true...

"IN THE CITY AND IN THE WILDERNESS I'VE BEEN BETRAYED BY FALSE BELIEVERS...

"I'VE SUFFERED HUNGER AND THIRST, COLDNESS AND NAKEDNESS...

"BUT IN ALL THIS...

"ONE THING I WILL DO FOREVER..."

He went on to Spain where he proclaimed the message of Yeshua and...

In A.D. 66, four years before the fall of Jerusalem, he died the death of a martyr in Rome.

CHARACTER PROFILES

Messiah Yeshua

The Savior, who overcame crucifixion and death through his resurrection power. He appeared to many afterward in various places. People placed their hope in him, and all who met him after he was raised from the dead experienced a great change of heart.

Peter

When Yeshua said, "I will build my Church upon this rock," he was referring to Peter. In Yeshua's name, Peter performed many miracles, and the foundation of the church was laid. It was exactly as Yeshua said.

Paul

His former name was Saul, and he was a born-and-bred Jew. Although he started out as a belligerent persecutor who was determined to wipe out the name of Yeshua, he encountered Yeshua on the road to Damascus and changed his heart. After that, he became a bold preacher of Yeshua's name and resurrection. Although he caused a ruckus everywhere he went, it didn't faze him. He was determined to live the rest of his life to preach his Savior, Yeshua.

Stephen

Stephen was a man filled with the Spirit and wisdom. In accordance with his duty, he daily rationed out food to all who gathered. Although he was loved by the townspeople, others were jealous and had him stoned to death. He became the first martyr for the faith, but before taking his last breath, he witnessed Yeshua standing at the right hand of God the Father.

Mark

Mark was born in Jerusalem. He accompanied his cousin Barnabas on Paul's first missionary journey, but he left them along the way. Eventually maturing under Barnabas's guidance, he became an interpreter and secretary, actively participating in the work of the faith alongside Paul and Peter. Later he wrote the Gospel of Mark.

Barnabas

Barnabas was a citizen of Cyprus and a pioneer evangelist. Although fearing post-conversion Paul, he arranged a meeting between Paul and Peter, which eventually led to Paul's being accepted among the apostles. He recognized Paul's gift as an evangelist and accompanied him on his first missionary journey.

Cornelius

A Roman centurion and God-fearing man, Cornelius obeyed the angel of God and invited Peter to his home. There he believed in Yeshua and was baptized. He was the first Gentile to become a Christian.

Timothy

A young man whose father was Greek and mother was Jewish, he went along as an assistant on Paul's second and third missionary journeys.

Silas

As a helper replacing Barnabas, he accompanied Paul on his trip to Asia Minor. He was also known as a prophet.

Priscilla & Aquila

A Jewish couple whose occupation was tent-making, they met Paul in Corinth after Emperor Claudius ordered them to leave Rome, providing Paul with physical and spiritual care.

Luke

A physician who cared for Paul when he became ill at Troas, he accompanied Paul on his second and third missionary journeys and eventually chronicled these events in the Acts of the Apostles. He also wrote the Gospel of Luke.

CHRONOLOGY (A.D.)

About Year 30	Yeshua's crucifixion
.	The birth of Jerusalem church
About Year 32	Stephen's martyrdom
	Paul's conversion
About Year 34	Paul's first visit to Jerusalem
	Cornelius's conversion
About Year 42	The birth of the Antioch church
	(the first Gentile church)
About Year 47–48	Paul's first mission
	(to Galatia in Asia Minor)
About Year 48	Apostles' council at Jerusalem
Year 49–52	Paul's second mission
	(to Macedonia and Greece)
	Churches birthed at Philippi, Corinth, and Thessalonica
Year 54–57	Paul's third mission
	(to Greece and west Asia Minor)
Year 57	Paul to Macedonia
Year 57–58	Paul to Corinth
Year 58–60	Paul's stay at Caesarea
Year 60–61	Paul to Rome
Year 61–63	Paul's imprisonment in Rome
	Peter and Paul martyred in Rome
Year 64	Persecution by Nero
Year 66–70	Coming Jewish war
Year 70	Destruction of the Jewish Temple
Year 95	Persecution by Emperor Domitian
Year 313	Recognition of the Christian church
Year 392	Christianity made state religion in Roman Empire

Letters to the Thessalonians 1 & 2

Letters to the Corinthians 1 & 2
Letter to the Galatians
Letter to the Philippians
Letter to Philemon
Letter to the Ephesians
Letter to the Colossians
Letter to the Romans

Letters of Peter 1 & 2
Letter of James
Letter to the Hebrews

Letters to Timothy 1 & 2
Letter to Titus
Letter of Jude

Revelation of John

287